– Huge Selection Online and In-Stock
– 100's of Brand Names
– Exclusive Designs
– No Sales Tax*

– ALA Certified Customer Service
– Free Shipping Available
– Ships Next Business Day
– Volume Discounts for Builders

*Excluding Washington and Idaho

for **Indoor Lighting**

for **Outdoor Lighting**

When you're *ready to detail –*

shop **DestinationLighting.com**

Awarded *2008 ENERGY STAR®*
PARTNER OF THE YEAR - LIGHTING SHOWROOM

Bob Greenspan
architectural photography

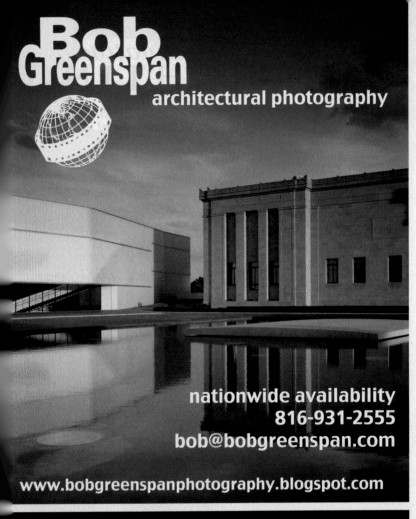

nationwide availability
816-931-2555
bob@bobgreenspan.com

www.bobgreenspanphotography.blogspot.com

ICON architecture/planning inc.

American Institute of Architects • NCARB

FROM **CONCEPT** TO **COMPLETION**

The award-winning firm of ICON architecture/planning, inc., headed by Principal Architect Dan L. Goodrich, has been successfully involved in the design of projects for the past 18 years.

Our business philosophy is based upon providing thorough information, accuracy and integrity of design, combined with reliable, personal service to our clients. Our office employs the latest technology in Internet communications, Computer Aided Design & Drafting (CADD), Energy Analysis, Cost Analysis, and Proven CSI Specifications and Scheduling Systems, which provide you with the highest quality documents and services available at equitable fees.

Our design team consists of professionals focused on value engineering while utilizing a broad scope of experience in residential and commercial projects. We strive to provide personal, efficient, courteous service and cost efficient solutions and we are prepared to serve you with every diligence that I'm sure you will expect.

Single-Family • Multi-Family • Mixed-Use • Commercial • Hospitality

Tel: 503.534.0337	Boones Ferry Crossing
Fax: 503.534.0339	17040 Pilkington Road, Suite 211
E-mail: info@iconarchitect.com	Lake Oswego, Oregon 97035

WWW.ICONARCHITECT.COM

AMDA PRESS

President:	*Alan Mascord*
Vice President:	*Donna Mascord*
General Manager:	*Jon Epley*
Publisher:	*Amy Fullwiler*
Creative Director:	*Diane Arthur Kukish*
Graphic Designers:	*Kim Campeau, Gary Higginbotham*
Website Design:	*Kevin Banton*
Customer Service Manager:	*Joelle Irvine*
Director of Home Design:	*Eric Schnell*
Plan Production Manager:	*Marie Adams*
Senior Drafting Technician:	*Randy Voeller*
Writers:	*Carol Shea, David Cohen, Mary Afeman, Gary Higginbotham, Matthew Daby*
Illustrators:	*Aaron Johnson, John Russell*
Photographers:	*Bob Greenspan, Christine Banton, Alan Mascord*
Customer Service:	*(503) 225-9161 sales@mascord.com Toll Free: (800) 411-0231*
Advertising Inquiries:	*(503) 225-9161 x 255 advertising@mascord.com*
To Order Plans:	*(800) 411-0231*
Website Address:	*www.mascordlivingspaces.com*

©2008 Mascord Living Spaces, published by AMDA Press. All rights reserved. No part of this publication may be reproduced, by any means without written permission by the publisher. All floor plans and elevations ©Alan Mascord Design Associates, Inc. and may not be reproduced without consent of the designer.

AMDA Press corporate office: 1815 NW Overton Street, Portland, Oregon 97209

Printed in the United States of America

First Printing February 2008

10 9 8 7 6 5 4 3 2

ISBN softcover: 0-9788113-0-5

THE RIGHT PRODUCTS, FOR THE RIGHT APPLICATIONS.

by Weyerhaeuser

Trus Joist TJI® Joist

There's more to floor performance than just meeting code – the floor makes the first impression about the quality of the whole house. That is why TJI joists are engineered for consistency and durability.

Trus Joist TimberStrand® LSL

TimberStrand LSL works for almost every application – wall and roof framing, rim board, door and window headers, as well as beams or columns. Try Zone Framing and save the TimberStrand LSL for the areas or "zones" that have to be absolutely straight, like tall walls, kitchens, and tiled bathrooms.

Trus Joist Parallam® PSL

Used for beams, columns, headers, or posts, Parallam PSL's strength is the perfect solution for high-load situations. For exteriors, try Wolmanized Parallam PSL, treated with Copper Azole-type B (CA-B) preservative all the way into the core of its cross section to resist insects and decay.

NEW! iLevel® Shear Brace

iLevel Shear Brace protects against damage from lateral forces. It features high allowable loads and narrow widths, mutli-story applications, can be trimmed or shimmed for custom heights, and is engineered wood which has an ideal nailing surface. All of which affords greater design flexibility.

Microllam® LVL Beams

Microllam LVL beams work well in applications all over the house. They can easily be built-up on site to cut down on the heavy lifting associated with beams. No matter where they're used, they install quickly with little or no waste. They're made from our proven Microllam laminated veneer lumber (LVL). This means they're very stable and they resist warping, splitting and shrinking.

iLevel and the Environment

iLevel is part of Weyerhaeuser. As owners and stewards of vast amounts of forest lands we strongly believe in promptly replanting after harvesting trees to ensure the availability of forests for future generations. Each year, Weyerhaeuser harvests only 1-3 percent of its timberlands and plants more than 100 million seedlings, creating sustainably managed forests. We also embrace ecological responsibilities including soil stability, water quality and wildlife habitat. That is first class, perpetual forestry and we are committed to it.

SUSTAINABLE
FORESTRY
INITIATIVE

contents

Shown on these pages are the finely crafted details of
PLAN L02-2458, see more on page 24.
Photography ©Bob Greenspan

Welcome to the 2008 Issue of Living Spaces

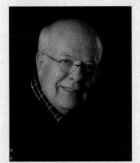

This second edition of Living Spaces comes to you during one of the more difficult and discouraging home-building markets in recent memory. However, I want to inspire you here with some exciting, timely and hopefully encouraging ideas. The challenges that you face today can also become terrific opportunities. We have focused on developing new plans, programs and services that will help give you an edge in this tight market.

The "Green" building movement gets a lot of press these days. Much of what you see may be interesting but often they are one-off, contemporary projects and you to think to yourself…."this might be a hard sell in my neighborhood". We need to bring "Green" building into the mainstream and to do this we've assembled a team of experts who are passionate about "Green". Through an exciting partnership with **The Whirlpool Corporation**, we've written a book, ***Mascord Efficient Living***, and developed the **Efficient Living Program**, which demystifies the "Green" construction process and enables you to get your project certified. Learn more about this on page 8.

We're happy to announce our renewed partnership with our friends at **iLevel by Weyerhaeuser** and the continued process of adding **iLevel Trus Joist Floor Framing Plans** to all our new plans. In addition, we continue to sweep through our most popular designs and will eventually provide this value-added product to all our plans.

This is a prolific year for us here at AMDA with about 80 new plans to add to our collection, including a couple Street of Dreams homes that truly illustrate that "Green" construction can be beautiful and suit many different styles and neighborhoods.

You want contemporary? We have broken out a small section that features some new contemporary examples, including AMDA Design Director Eric Schnell's own new home, plan 21113. Starting on page 60, this is a striking example of efficient living. Traditional neighborhoods are not going away but the younger generation is attracted to good contemporary designs and we feel this is a small but growing segment of the housing market that is not currently being met by the plans of yesterday.

Beginning on page 82, you'll find a new section devoted to neighborhood design. Here, several different approaches illustrate how an attractive community can be created to suit different markets and styles. When developing a new community, our staff can choose a selection of stock plans for you, or if unable to find the exact product, our designers can create some new designs specifically for your market. And, through our sister company, AMDA Press, we can help you to market your project effectively.

Most homebuyers have a difficult time understanding two dimensional drawings, so consider having us create Google® SketchUp models of the important spaces in your homes, giving you an important edge in the marketplace. Some examples of this can be found on page 11 and 52.

The difficult market we find ourselves in calls for a different strategy to sell your homes – let us help you take advantage of the opportunities you have to set yourselves apart from the crowd….give yourself an edge!

Your design partner

Alan Mascord, President

innovation

SOME BUSINESSES RESIST CHANGE.
OTHERS MAKE CHANGE HAPPEN.
WHICH WILL YOU WORK WITH?

Technology can't solve every problem. The key is to find areas where it can help. And that's just what we're doing at iLevel — a new business from Trus Joist, Structurwood and Weyerhaeuser. We've developed new products and software, allowing us to customize the structural framing materials you need. Which helps minimize callbacks and reduce jobsite waste. Learn more at iLevel.com.

Visit our iLevel Design-Partner, Alan Mascord Design Associates, at one of their Home Design Centers, or call toll free at 1-866-512-1157.

PORTLAND, OR 1305 NW 18th Ave. • Portland, OR 97209 • 503-225-9161

RENTON, WA 1000 Oakesdale Ave., Suite 115 • Renton, WA 98057 • 425-277-7501

iLevel™
Trus Joist + Structurwood + Weyerhaeuser

Mascord
ALAN MASCORD DESIGN ASSOCIATES, INC.

Weyerhaeuser®, Structurwood®, and Trus Joist® are registered trademarks and iLevel™ is a trademark of Weyerhaeuser Company, Federal Way, Washington. © 2006 Weyerhaeuser Company. All rights reserved.

Weyerhaeuser

mascord efficient living
Sustainability with *Style*

Mascord Efficient Living is a set of tools and resources to help you build a more energy efficient, sustainable and healthy home.

As home owners, home builders, and home designers, our individual lifestyles greatly inform our decisions to buy, to build, and to create. In addition, we're becoming increasingly conscious of how these same lifestyles impact our environment. Whether spurred by economic pressures, education, or as a result of world events and first hand experiences—our individual desires to live responsibly are catching up with a collective need to live more efficiently.

Rest assured, *efficient living* does not mean radically changing your lifestyle. Small steps towards sustainability need not impact your individuality and lifestyle choices. Whether you prefer traditional, contemporary, minimalist, or more eclectic styles—for each individual style there is a way to live more efficiently. In line with your unique style, making small and educated decisions at key points along the buying and building processes can result in a vast improvement in efficiency; you'll also find that sustainable choices result in significant financial savings.

The key is to be educated about the purchases you make. In addition to the initial purchase price, it's important to know how a product works for you, where a product comes from, what you will do with it when you are done, and how much it costs for you to operate.

Armed with this knowledge, you will be able to make smart decisions to improve your financial position, to keep your family and environment safe, and to create a space that best reflects your style. Companies such as Alan Mascord Design Associates and Whirlpool® Corporation are responding to environmental concerns by designing homes and products for efficiency and durability, without discounting the ever-present importance of maintaining individual style. While it may seem intuitive, these efficient products and homes really do operate better, last longer, save you money, and are better for the environment. Building a *Mascord Efficient Living* home has never been a smarter, more practical, or more customizable endeavor.

Available for purchase with any plan from the entire Mascord collection, Mascord Efficient Living makes it easier than ever to build green. In addition to setting the bar for your environmentally conscientious home, the Mascord Efficient Living package makes it a breeze to build green and also earn valuable green building certifications such as LEED®, NGBS™, or ENERGY STAR.

The construction and operation of homes in the U.S. is one of the largest contributors of energy consumption and environmentally harmful waste, and many people are looking carefully at the construction of their homes to allow lower energy bills, protect the environment and live healthier. These attitudes toward sustainable practices have created a large market demand for green homes. Energy prices continue to rise, and educated through first hand experiences, news, and other media, the American public have become aware of how their lifestyles affect the environment. two-thirds of all homeowners are aware of green building.

Satisfaction with green homes is extremely high: over 85% of green home owners are likely to recommend a green home to others.

The total green building marketplace is expected to be worth up to $60 Billion by 2010 (one in ten new building starts). In a struggling housing market, green features differentiate your home in the marketplace.

The Mascord Efficient Living Book

To help you get started on your way to a more efficient lifestyle, Alan Mascord Design Associates presents *Mascord Efficient Living*—a book of over 50 innovative house plans that meet and exceed national green building standards, including LEED® for Homes, National Green Building Standard™, and ENERGY STAR®.

In this book, you'll learn:

- How to incorporate principles of design with healthy living choices

- How to utilize renewable materials and expend less energy

- How to maximize the latest technology and recycling methods

- The basic concepts, ideas and theories behind green building, design and sustainable living

- Things to consider before, during and after the construction of your home

This book also includes a CD featuring:

- Google™ SketchUp software, for customizing 3D kitchen plans

- 3D kitchen models featuring the Digital Green™ Portfolio and Google 3D Warehouse interactive features

- Access to support and required forms for green building certification

- Access to over 500 more efficient house plans

Whether you're designing your dream home, considering building materials and appliances, or simply looking to lower your monthly utility costs—*Mascord Efficient Living* gives you the "GREEN" light you've been waiting for.

Partnering with Whirlpool® and Google® SketchUp™

Alan Mascord Design Associates is proud to partner with **Whirlpool® Corporation**, the industry leader in ENERGY STAR compliance, in the design of this collection. Its very creation represents the coming together of design leaders who share a commitment to both sustainable goals and using technology in bringing home plans to life.

In our view, the more affordable sustainable home designs become, the greater the difference we can make. In other words, as more homes save energy, conserve water and promote good indoor air quality—the better for all of us. The goal of both Alan Mascord Design Associates and Whirlpool® Corporation is to make building green a reality for the many, not the few.

Following that thought, it can be a challenging process to translate any kind of home plan, green or not, from a dream drawn on paper to an actual dwelling place. That's why Whirlpool® Corporation has taken advantage of technology like Google® SketchUp™ . Google® SketchUp™ is a design and visualization tool primarily used by architects and designers. However, its quick and easy features mean you don't have to be an industry professional to use it.

The software, which is on the CD-ROM in the back of the *Mascord Efficient Living* book, better enables you to visualize a home before building it—and in 3D! What's more, it also allows you a fast and fun way to explore energy—and water-efficient kitchen and laundry appliance options from the Whirlpool® Corporation family of brands, including Jenn-Air®, KitchenAid® and Whirlpool®.

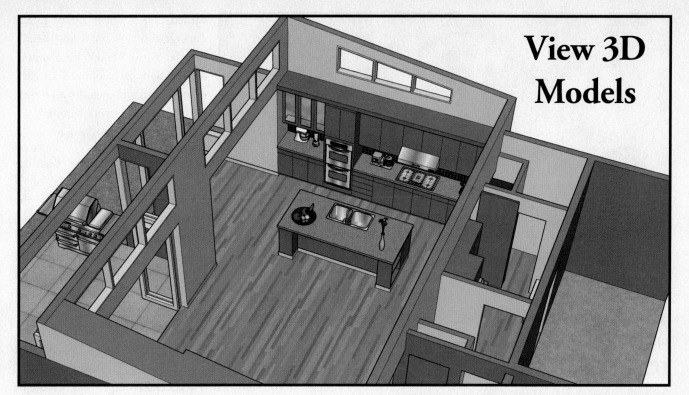

Introducing the Digital Green™ Portfolio

Long before green was so much a part of the popular conscious, Whirlpool® Corporation embraced the concept of acting responsibly as a steward of the environment. It was simply the right thing to do, and it still is. Today, Whirlpool® is a leader in harnessing technology to realize sustainable goals, and they have focused special attention in a very logical place. The place where ideas are formed and crucial choices are made: the area of design.

The Digital Green™ Portfolio from Whirlpool® Corporation offers cutting-edge, internet-based tools that make it easier to create and visualize projects—right down to choosing appliances. Two components within the portfolio that make this streamlining possible deserve a closer look: the Green Appliance Collection and the Green Home Collection.

The Green Appliance Collection

The Green Appliance Collection is a select subcategory of all the virtual appliance models that Whirlpool Corporation has created and placed in a vast library of digital models called the Google® 3D Warehouse. Using Google® SketchUp™ software, anyone can go to the Google® 3D Warehouse and integrate appliances into their plans at the very earliest stages of the design process. The technology works so easily that you can get in on this interactive exploration, too.

The Digital Green Portfolio not only contains appliances, but fully realized home designs as well. Aptly named the Green Home Collection—and including plans by Alan Mascord Design Associates—it's a virtual gallery of homes showcasing the latest in sustainable practices.

As with the Green Appliance Collection, the Green Home Collection comes alive via Google® SketchUp™ and the Google® 3D Warehouse. The technology allows you to take virtual home tours in 3D.

The CD included with this book contains the software and files you'll need. The steps are easy and the software is user-friendly. Once you're up and running, you can explore many of the kitchen plans in this book in 3D, and even experiment with different appliance models by going to the Google® 3D Warehouse. No matter whether you're a home-seeker or industry pro, the whole idea is to interact, explore, engage and customize. Not only to bring sustainability down to earth, but also to more closely suit individual wants, needs and preferences.

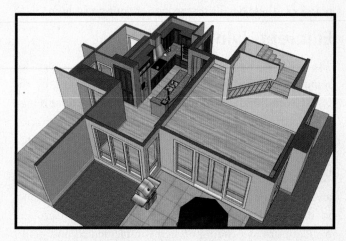

How to build with *Mascord Efficient Living*™

With the purchase of a *Mascord Efficient Living* package, you receive detailed drawings and notes, along with additional information which will ease you through the process of building your "green" home step-by-step. The first step to realizing your Efficient Living Home is to choose your path. We offer three paths that help you build an efficient, healthy home or certify it to meet leading industry standards.

Efficient Living BASIC

Designed for those not pursuing a national certification, *The Efficient Living BASIC Package* includes notes and details to meet or exceed guidelines for energy efficiency set by the U.S. Environmental Protection Agency as required for ENERGY STAR. These homes are at least 15% more energy efficient than homes built to the 2004 International Residential Code (IRC). In addition, notes and details specify site considerations, alternate building envelope systems, choices to improve energy efficiency, water efficiency, and indoor air quality, and methods of construction to meet sustainable practices. These details set the bar for your green home.

Efficient Living LEED

The LEED® Rating System is a nationally recognized standard for green building created and managed by the U.S. Green Building Council. Points are awarded for design and construction practices in 8 categories: Innovation and Design, Location and Linkages, Sustainable Sites, Water Efficiency, Energy and Atmosphere, Materials and Resources, Indoor Environmental Quality, and Awareness and Education. LEED® for Homes™ certification comes in differing levels of complexity, ranging from 'Certified' to 'Platinum' depending on items implemented and points

earned. *The Efficient Living LEED Package* contains notes and details specific to the LEED® for Homes™ certification path, options to earn extra points, and includes all forms, notices and paperwork required.

Efficient Living NGBS

The National Green Building Standard™ is the result of a cooperative effort between the National Association of Home Builders and the International Code Council. Points are awarded for design and construction practices in 6 categories: Lot Design and Preparation, Resource Efficiency, Energy Efficiency, Water Efficiency, Indoor Environmental Quality, and Operation, Maintenance and Owner Education. Awards range from 'Certified' to Emerald', depending on items implemented and points earned. *The Efficient Living NGBS Package* contains notes and details specific to the NAHB NGBS™ certification path, options to earn extra points, and includes all forms, notices and paperwork required.

Package Information:

What the package includes:

Notes and Details Sheets

We supply calculated specifications based on your particular home plan, notes and details to follow during construction, and quality management tools to ensure the result you require is communicated to your team. These plan pages describe, in detail, how to construct your home to meet your chosen green building standard. Specific details show how to construct your home with:

An efficient and tight building envelope through advanced wall, floor and roof systems that will discourage water intrusion, mold growth, and air infiltration.

High performing mechanical systems to save on utilities, keep the home comfortable in all seasons, and promote healthy indoor air quality.

Healthy, durable, and environmentally friendly materials on the inside and outside of the home.

Environmentally sensitive and respectful landscaping and site planning.

Project Information File

This supplemental information includes details about certification standards, your guide to using the Efficient Living plan set and achieving certification, forms to give vendors, sub-contractors, and officials; and information for the homeowner. In essence, everything you need to get your green home built and certified!

Consultation

Initial package purchase price includes a one-hour phone conference or personal meeting with a Mascord Efficient Living Support Team member to get you on track and to help answer any questions. Additional consultation is available for an additional fee.

Access to online information

Our Mascord Efficient Living website includes sections containing up-to-date product and information resources accessible to our builders and homeowners.

Listing on Mascord Efficient Living website

After completing your Mascord Efficient Living home, your project and details can be posted on our website. Showcase the project you are proud of, and builders—let consumers know you are available for green building construction projects!

Plus, the Mascord Efficient Living Hardback Book and CD-Rom!

With your first package purchase, we include a copy of the Mascord Efficient Living book and accompanying CD. With the foreword written by acclaimed author Sarah Susanka, this book provides an overview of the theories, philosophies and reasons behind green building, things to consider when building a sustainable home, and tips for living in one thereafter.

Ordering Information:

Before you order a Mascord Efficient Living Plan Package: Determine which path you are going to pursue for your green home. For help, review the comparison between standards included in this information brochure. For specific information, contact the governing bodies noted in the contacts section.

Your Mascord Efficient Living Plan Package pages will contain notes and details to follow for your specific chosen standard. If you change certification tracks after plan purchase, charges may be incurred. Be aware that changing paths after the start of construction may not be possible due to certification requirements.

When you're ready to place your order:

Call (503) 225-9161 to speak to one of our representatives, or visit www.mascordefficientliving.com

Lakeside Custom Homes

Turning Dreams to Reality

Tracy Schmitt, of Lakeside Custom Homes, has been around construction all of his life.

After working in the trade for many years, Tracy started his own construction company in 1992, later establishing Lakeside Custom Homes in 2001. With over 40 completed Mascord homes under his belt, Tracy has fine tuned his skills by completing the Master Builders Course, and continues to hone his skills further by researching and implementing new and innovative construction practices — such as utilizing the Mascord Efficient Living program.

Tracy prides himself on being able to build homes with a fresh twist that meet the needs of his customers. "We have enjoyed working with Alan Mascord Design Associates and their team. They are always in pursuit of taking care of their clients and making everybody feel like we're one big team together. This means a lot to me. Putting a team together is the most important thing you can do. It lays the foundation for a smooth start." he says.

How long have you been building Mascord homes?

Lakeside has been building Mascord plans since its inception, but Tracy began using Mascord plans even in his early days of building, over a decade ago.

Which area of the country do you build in?

We build primarily in Clackamas County, near Portland, Oregon – that includes Happy Valley, Lake Oswego West Linn, Stafford, and Beaver Creek. We also build in Bend and Central Oregon.

Which plans have you built?

2263 and 2263B, 2365, 2228AC, 2223AF, 2223AD, 22151AA, 2358, 1403, 2247F, 22111C, 2208C, 2206A, 1314, 2366, 2345 2258D, 22122B, and several versions of plan 2270 and many more.

Which were your favorites?

2263B, 2358, & 2270.

Why? These plans were our favorites because of the way they seem to flow seamlessly from one room to another. 2358 has a wonderful open feeling to it and 2263B and 2270 are just such beautiful craftsman style homes.

What finishing touches did you add for your client?

Whether a home is a custom or a spec we love to add many custom touches to them. We always include beautiful woodwork in our homes from wainscoting in a dining room or den to crown molding on tray ceilings. The open staircases are finished with wrought iron balusters and custom built newels. It's especially important to create a grand entrance so I use very elaborate entry door systems with sidelights, transoms and custom millwork surrounding them. We use natural stone such as travertine and slate throughout, along with granite countertops in the kitchens. We finish our homes off with gorgeous light fixtures to compliment the style of the home. On our exteriors, we use a combination of stone, shake and siding to give each home its own unique look.

What do you like about Mascord Plans?

AMDA is so in tune to the needs of our clients, and present plans that satisfy the needs of the area in which we build. Each plan seems to be very well thought out and flows well to create a very livable space.

What do your customers think of the finished homes?

We have always received very positive feedback from our homeowners. They love the style and livability of their new homes. Many have said they would want us to build their next home.

What do you like about working with Mascord?

We feel very fortunate to be able to work with a company like Mascord on such a personal level. Whether it's the front desk or the designers themselves, we always feel like they are just a phone call away and they will help us with any issues that may arise during a project. The service has been outstanding. The staff at Mascord has gone above and beyond to meet our needs.

Tracy Schmitt can be contacted at (503) 946-8310 or visit www.lakesidecustomhomesinc.com.

Below, The Lakeside Custom Home Team, left to right: Carol Ostrom, Tracy Schmitt and Stephanie Snell

Building a Home that Blends Modern
Conveniences with Old-World Craftsman Charm

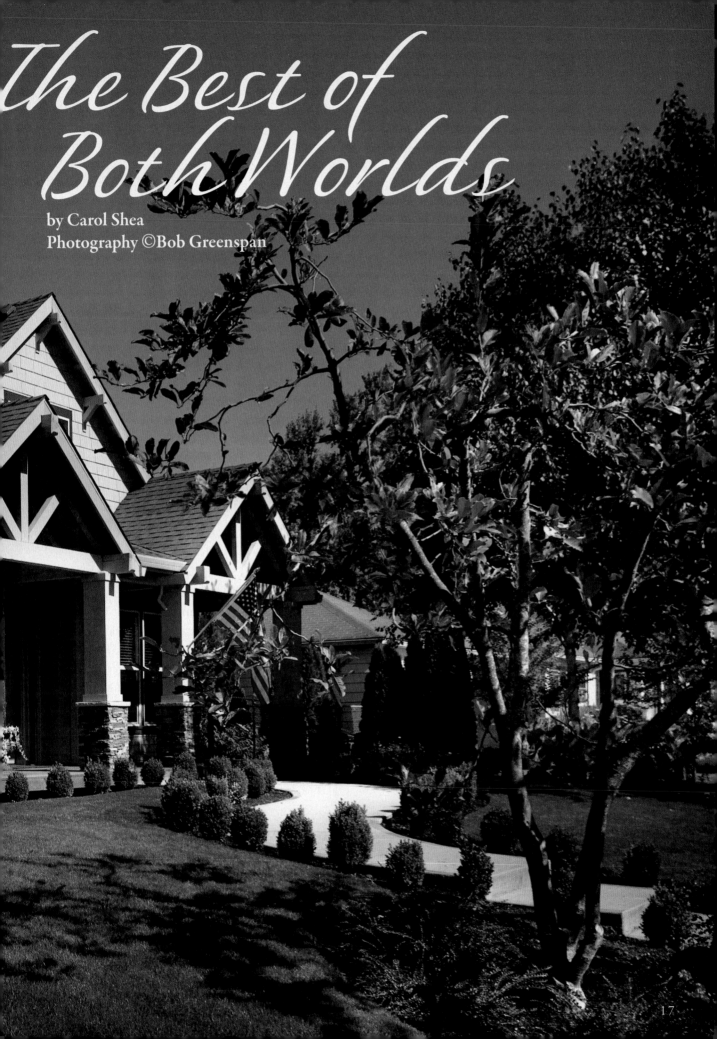

The Best of Both Worlds

by Carol Shea
Photography ©Bob Greenspan

The two-story spaces of the great room and entry draw in daylight and they channel traffic to the more intimate spaces of the kitchen and nook and the front dining room and office.

When plans for remodeling their historic home proved beyond their reach, Annette and Charles Chapman built an updated Arts and Crafts-inspired home while staying in the neighborhood they loved.

The Edgewood Park neighborhood near downtown Vancouver, Washington offered Annette and Charles Chapman everything they wanted: a view of the Columbia River, walking distance to the downtown area, and close proximity to Officer's Row, a pictorial, tree-lined street filled with restored historic homes that once served as housing for soldiers, officers, and families stationed at Vancouver Barracks. So when Annette, a real estate agent, came across a 1906 property for sale in the area, she bought it without hesitation—even though her husband Charles hadn't even seen it. "I had to make a decision right then and there and he wasn't there," Annette says with a laugh.

Charles wasn't disappointed, though. He too was attracted to the distinctiveness, convenience, and character of the neighborhood.

The Edgewood Park area was a much better fit for their personal taste and professional lifestyle. With so many positive features to the area, Annette and Charles felt they had settled in their dream location. After eight years, they could only find one thing that wasn't ideal about Edgewood Park: their house.

At just 700 square feet, the 1906 structure was cramped, even for just two people and their pets. In the interest of restoring the historic structure, they considered remodeling, but ran into a host of costly challenges. The home's ancient plumbing was stapled to the outside walls in a retrofit that would require a complete redo; the wiring was a mishmash of out-of-date technologies that also dictated starting over—especially if they wanted the capabilities to handle today's technologies. But the nail in the coffin for their remodeling

The original 1906 structure, though rustic and charming, was too cramped for two people.

hopes was a crumbling basement foundation, the repair costs of which proved exorbitant.

Tearing down the aging structure and building a new home, was the couples' next best option. Starting with paper and pencil, the Chapmans began sketching their ideas onto paper. Annette and Charles had three main criteria for their new home: a side-load garage, a main-floor master suite, and a dining nook that faced the early morning light. With the newest home in the neighborhood being 50 years old, having an exterior that blended in with the historic styles of the neighborhood was also an important consideration.

The couple took their search online and found plan 2270CA from Alan Mascord Design Associates, Inc. "The plan matched almost exactly to what we wanted as far as the floor plan. The outside looked a bit different, but the floor plan was almost exactly the same," Charles says. The home's Craftsman-inspired exterior was appropriate for the neighborhood.

Another advantage of the floor plan is its compact footprint. Even with its three-car garage and a main-level master suite—both of which often add width to the typical home—this design is less than 55 feet wide and just 54 feet deep, making it especially ideal for a restrictive infill lot, such as in the Chapmans' case.

Defined by its twin gables straddling the front porch, the facade recalls a mix of design styles, according to Alan Mascord, of Alan Mascord Design Associates, Inc. "The exterior is an attractive mix of Arts and Crafts, Rustic, and Lodge styles all blended together...The appeal [of the exterior] is mainly the heavy timberwork in the front gables."

In order to save money and include the upgrades they wanted, Charles and Annette decided to take on the role of building the home themselves. The project took just over a

Almost immediately upon entering the Chapman's home, one experiences the home's airy feel, made manifest through views of the upper-story balcony and wall of windows beyond.

year to complete, a remarkable feat for owner-contractors, considering that the first month was spent tearing down the home and salvaging the materials to a friend. And even though the time commitment was demanding, the couple points out the many benefits of building their own home. "We did a lot of upgrades," Charles says. "When you do it yourself, you see why some builders put in vinyl and square granite instead of slab. It all adds up and it cuts into your profit. But when you're doing it yourself, you can do the upgrades that you want.

Their beautiful home is a testament to their hands-on oversight of the project. Naturally stained oak floors and vertical-grain fir trim serve as backdrop for the nature-inspired colors of the entry, kitchen, and great room. These public areas serve as the gateway into the home and provide the main living and entertaining spaces. The openness is a welcome change from their former tiny home, Charles says.

Open free-flowing spaces creates a great house for entertaining.

Frequent entertainers, Annette and Charles customized the public areas to suit their entertaining style. During the holidays, the couple erected a 16-foot Christmas tree in the great room, the size and stature of which proved stunning for a neighborhood party they hosted. "It's really a nice place to entertain," Annette adds. "You can have 40 people in here and there's plenty of room for them to mill around. It's a great house for entertaining."

To accommodate their serving needs, the couple modified the kitchen layout to include a 4x7-foot island that provides a large space to prepare food and display buffet-style appetizers.

The Chapmans kept the television out of the great room, preferring to emphasize connecting and conversing, rather than television viewing, when they are hosting guests. Instead, the television is located in one of the upper-level bedrooms, which was converted into a living space. "It's a different lifestyle," Charles says. "Most people have a giant nook right next to the fireplace. But we just didn't want to have a TV as a main focus when you have guests over."

In the absence of media equipment, an upright, antique piano serves as a conversation piece, along with the spectacular wall of windows along the rear. "[The window wall] lets in a lot of light," Charles says. "During the daytime, I never turn on any lights because there is so much light that comes in."

At times, the bay breakfast nook, which Charles wanted to face the early-morning light, gets so much sunlight, the Chapmans find themselves lowering the blinds for light control.

The upper-level bonus room was finished as an exercise room, complete with rubberized floor and vaulted ceiling for jumping rope. The other upper-level bedroom is used as a guest room. The main-level master suite is tucked behind the garage and next to the public areas, granting access to all of the main rooms without the need for traveling up and down a staircase. The arrangement gives Annette and Charles the option to live in the home even if traveling the staircase becomes cumbersome.

The home's den and dining room also were important features of the floor plan to Annette and Charles. The dining room houses their formal Craftsman-style dining room furniture and is used on holidays, special occasions, and dinner parties. The den functions as the couple's home office, where Annette runs her real estate business.

Expanding the living spaces to the outdoors are two bluestone patios, one in the backyard and one in the side yard. The Chapman's worked with a neighbor friend who is a master gardener to help them plan an area replete with lush vegetation, privacy hedges, and flowering perennials.

Now that Annette and Charles have a beautiful home to match their ideal neighborhood they describe themselves as "home bodies." They say rather be home than almost anywhere—just as it should be.

Annette and Charles Chapman at home with their two fur-kids, Dakota and Ginger.

Darchwood
PLAN L02-2270CA

Upper Floor	673 Sq. Ft.
Main Floor	1,785 Sq. Ft.
Sub-Total	2,485 Sq. Ft.
Bonus Room	+184 Sq. Ft.

Included Foundation *Crawlspace*

Please note: Photographed homes may have been changed to suit homeowners preference.

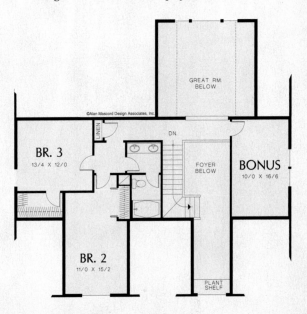

An antique piano makes an attractive focal point in the great room, where the Chapmans prefer to entertain and live rather than watch television. Annette picked up the accompanying stool with cowboy boot legs at a local furniture store.

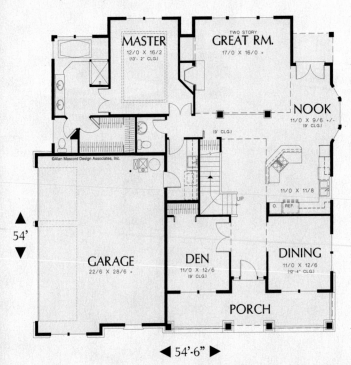

54'

54'-6"

Wrought-iron spindles on the staircase introduce a spark of interest in the entrance and serve as an antidote to the ample woodwork found throughout the home.

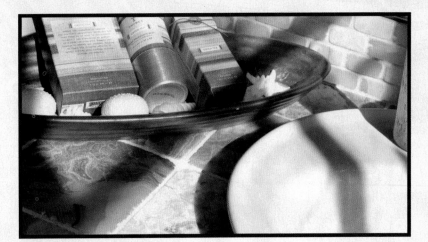

THE 2008 COLLECTION

Featuring

Alan Mascord Design Associates proudly presents our 2008 collection of home plans. In this brand new selection of exceptionally crafted homes, you'll find the inspiration you need to conceptualize and construct your dream home, no matter how classic or distinctive that dream might be. Our 2008 collection includes a rich variety of floor plans, each one fresh off the AMDA press with the level of quality and artistry that has become synonymous with the Alan Mascord name.

In thirty years of designing some of the most extraordinary floor plans on the market, our 2008 collection furthers our proven commitment to aesthetics and economy. These home plans have been designed to create structures and living spaces that are as elegant, luxurious and comfortable as they are economical and energy-efficient. Up to date for 2008, the following homes combine the most innovative home trends with the time-tested sustainability of our quality craftsmanship. Beautifully designed and comprehensively varied, our 2008 collection includes a wide array of some of our most impressive homes to date.

Along with their carefully chosen architectural elements and stunning curb appeal, Alan Mascord Design Associates has partnered with iLevel by Weyerhaeuser to ensure these "dream homes" offer the most dependable building products. Suitable for submission to local building departments, each plan offers structural floor framing plans from iLevel. Together, our commitment to quality and cost-consciousness ensures that these designs can become a part of your daily reality.

Photographs of more spectacular plans are available at
www.mascordlivingspaces.com

*Please note: Photographed homes may have been changed
to suit homeowner's preference*

PLAN L02-2458
Photography ©Bob Greenspan

Copper Falls
PLAN L02-2458

Built by Lockie Homes, Photography ©Bob Greenspan

Built for The Street of Dreams, The Copper Falls emphasizes natual beauty.

Elegant, simple lines and energy-conscious finishes harvest a natural air in this Craftsman-inspired home. Retaining the sturdy structural design and unalloyed materials revered in craftsman construction, our Copper Falls plan furthers an emphasis on natural grace. Particularly diligent consideration has been placed upon selecting eco-friendly materials and maintaining the highest possible indoor air/water quality, ensuring that this home's environmental impact will remain as clean as its lines suggest.

The home's materials reveal that quality of construction begins on the outside and continues within. You'll find indulgent details peppered throughout the interior, such as vaulted ceilings (in the great room, bonus room, and outdoor living space), generous built-ins, and a dramatic stone fireplace.

The free flowing floor plan offers an abundant amount of space while materials foster a cozy feel. Inside — deep, warm and reflective woods have been placed alongside specialty tile, granite and marble countertops, all made from post-consumer

recycled content. Built-in cabinetry, wood paneling, and stunning molding in the kitchen, dining room and den compliment the gorgeous flooring, composed of FSC certified wood. Where wood has not been installed, this home features environmentally friendly flooring alternatives such as cork, wool carpet, and extraordinarily handsome tile, found in the master bath.

Whether it is at dusk, dawn, or during a rapturous orange sunset— large, well-appointed, energy-rated windows beckon the light inside. An emphasis on energy and quality doesn't stop there, low-flow toilets, Energy-Star rated appliances, and an on-demand recirculation hot water system work to maintain clean air and conserve water. Outside, a pervious driveway and groundwater recharge system continue the home's effort towards efficiency.

A true retreat built to curb environmental impact, the Copper Falls home emphasizes classic beauty. In this warm and luxurious, Craftsman refuge, coming home is as much of an embrace to you as it is to your environment.

J Copper Falls
PLAN L02-2458

Upper Floor	2,150 Sq. Ft.
Main Floor	3,030 Sq. Ft.
Sub-Total	5,180 Sq. Ft.
Bonus Room	+908 Sq. Ft.
Incl. Foundation	Crawlspace

Please note: Photographed homes may have been changed to suit homeowners preference.

Featuring
Trus Joist • Structurwood • Weyerhaeuser

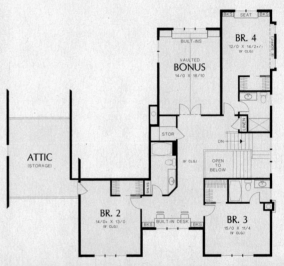

BR. 4
12/0 X 14/2+/-
(8' CLG.)

BKS   SEAT   BKS

BUILT-INS

VAULTED
BONUS
14/0 X 18/10

STOR

ATTIC
(STORAGE)

DN

(8' CLG.)

LINEN

OPEN
TO
BELOW

BR. 2
14/0+ X 13/0
(9' CLG.)

BKS   BUILT-IN DESK   BKS

BR. 3
15/0 X 11/4
(9' CLG.)

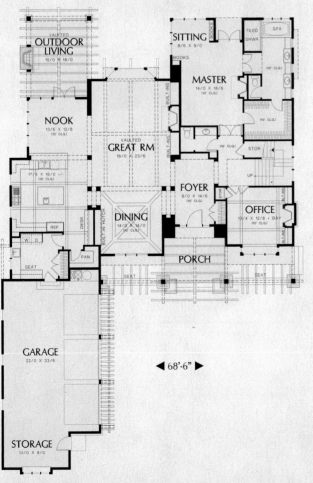

VAULTED
OUTDOOR
LIVING
15/0 X 18/0

SITTING
8/6 X 9/0   BOOKS   TILED   SPA
                      SHWR

BOOKS

MASTER
14/0 X 18/6
(10' CLG.)

(10' CLG.)

NOOK
13/6 X 12/6
(10' CLG.)

BUILT-INS

VAULTED
GREAT RM
18/0 X 23/6

(10' CLG.)

17/6 X 16/0 +/-
(10' CLG.)

STOR

UP

REF   DESK

BUILT IN HUTCH

DINING
14/0 X 14/0
(10' CLG.)

FOYER
9/0 X 14/6
(10' CLG.)

OFFICE
13/4 X 12/8 + BAY
(10' CLG.)

W. D.

PAN

SEAT

PORCH

SEAT   SEAT

GARAGE
22/0 X 33/6

◄ 68'-6" ►

STORAGE
13/0 X 8/0

Terrebonne
PLAN L02-2459

Built by Blazer Development, Photography ©Bob Greenspan

More than meets the eye...this Street of Dreams home is as eco-friendly, as it is beautiful.

From its French Country exterior and varied, sloping rooflines, to the rich plaster walls throughout, this home exudes Old-World charm. But a closer look reveals modern, energy-efficient enhancements that prove efficient living can also be luxurious.

The walkway and outer courtyard are paved with permeable pavers, which work in harmony with nature, both aesthetically and practically. The pavers allow water to filter naturally into the ground, reducing runoff and erosion tracks and replenishing

groundwater more effectively. They also dry more quickly than traditional pavement.

Once in the entryway, the warmth of authentic plaster walls greets you. Despite their beauty, these walls conceal a wealth of cost-effective, environmentally friendly qualities. Among other things, plaster is more durable, fire-retardant and resistant to mold. It can also cut your heating and cooling costs by its ability to retain and release heat more effectively than traditional sheetrock.

Overhead, the rough-hewn beams in the kitchen complete the impression of a rustic, richly appointed villa. But there is less to these beams than meets the eye. They are formed from individual reclaimed wooden planks, leaving them hollow inside, and more importantly, leaving timber from old-growth forests untouched. The kitchen's appliances all meet energy-efficient standards, saving precious resources while saving you money.

Outside, the ground is covered with artificial turf, which looks perpetually pristine with low maintenance. Looks aside, artificial turf eliminates the need for constant watering and mowing, which uses gas. Its preservation of two important resources makes it both cost-effective and energy efficient.

Herrebonne
PLAN L02-2459

Upper Floor	721 Sq. Ft.
Main Floor	3,631 Sq. Ft.
Total Area	4,352 Sq. Ft.
Incl. Foundation	*Crawlspace*

Please note: Photographed homes may have been changed to suit homeowners preference.

Featuring

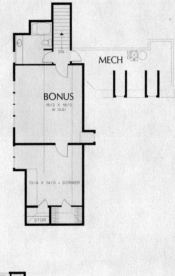

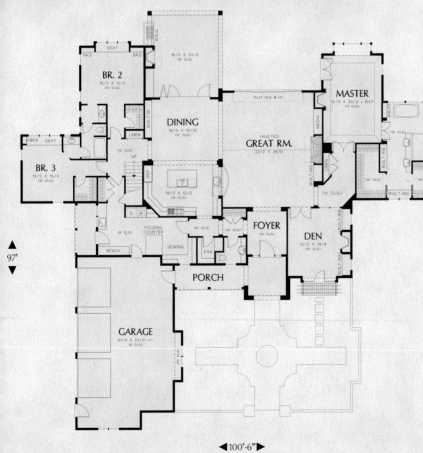

Timbersedge
PLAN L02-1411D

Built by West One Homes, Photography ©Bob Greenspan

Northwest-style and an emphasis on the outdoors meet contemporary, innovative design in this award-winning dream home.

An award-winner at the Street of Dreams, this breathtaking home incorporates the best elements of classic Northwest living in one open, richly detailed floor plan.

A lodge-inspired exterior sets a stunning emphasis on nature that continues throughout the home's indoor spaces. Views abound in nearly every room, where tall, oversized windows connect the interiors to their natural surroundings. A unique, outdoor kitchen area furthers a bond with the outdoors. Connecting to the large great room, which features a high, vaulted ceiling and generous built-ins, the two-island kitchen features an adjoining nook, built-in wine cooler and a separated, built-in desk area, which emphasizes the home's functionality—open, airy rooms have been designed to be as livable as they are they spacious.

Carefully chosen materials and detailed construction (from the home's millwork and beams to its floors and cabinetry) encourage a lodge-like feel — grand and lofty yet comfortable and rustic, this home feels as sweeping as a collection of tall Doug Firs while its contemporary, clean lines and well-used space create an impression of ease, comfort and simplicity.

Bedrooms are large and well appointed—a large master bedroom on the main features a lavish bathroom with oversized shower, spa, and connecting storage, which is a suite all its own—complete with ample

space and its very own washer/dryer. Three additional bedrooms reside on the lower level, alongside a unique wet bar and a wine cellar, which makes entertaining impressive for guests and a breeze for the homeowner.

Alongside its emphasis on nature, this home also incorporates innovative technology and state-of-the-art building practices — a stone mantle in the great room bears room for a seamlessly encased plasma television; a top of the line range and matching appliances in the kitchen create workspace equipped for a chef; the extensive wine cellar on the lower level fulfills any connoisseur's dream. In addition, this home takes advantage of the latest in home lighting design — soft, warm light comes from spots placed high above and equally pleasant, hanging fixtures illuminate counters and tables below.

In addition, this home features an office (complete with built-ins), a vaulted foyer and dining area, a lower level garden room, and plenty of outdoor space. A downstairs bonus room (which can be easily converted into a game room, playroom or home theatre) along with a sectioned-off laundry room and mudroom area off the garage rounds out this home's 5,000+ square feet of highly livable, rugged extravagance.

Jimbersedge
PLAN L02-1411D

Upper Floor	2,966 Sq. Ft.
Main Floor	2,189 Sq. Ft.
Sub-Total	5,155 Sq. Ft.
Bonus Room	+553 Sq. Ft.
Incl. Foundation	Daylight Basement

Please note: Photographed homes may have been changed to suit homeowners preference.

Featuring iLevel™
Trus Joist • Structurwood • Weyerhaeuser

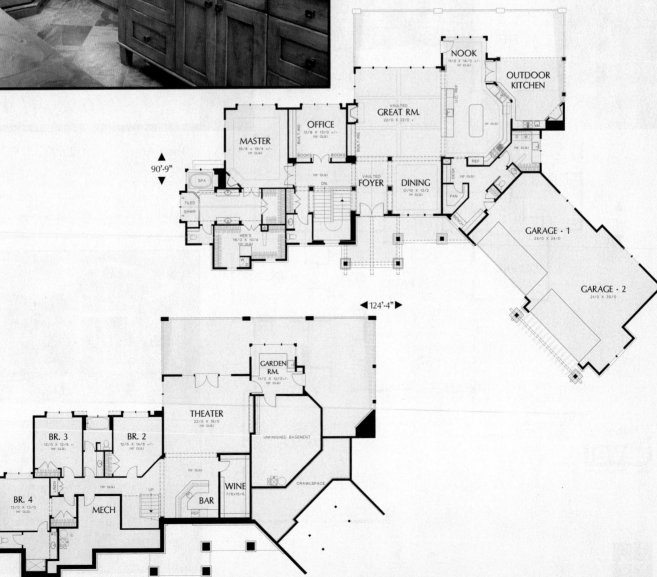

Plan L02-1237
The Skylar

Total Area   2,498 Sq. Ft.

Included Foundation   *Crawlspace*

Floor plan labels:

VAULTED
MASTER
15/0 X 16/0

SPA

(9' CLG.)

LIN

NICHE

MEDIA

NICHE

SHLVS

(9' CLG.)

LIN

VAULTED
GREAT RM.
21/0 X 24/6

DINING
11/6 X 14/6
(9' CLG.)

BUILT-IN

13/0 X 9/6 +
(9' CLG.)

REF

DESK

PAN

(9' CLG.)

VAULTED
BR. 2
12/6 X 15/0

VAULTED
DEN/BR. 3
13/0 X 11/6

PATIO

WROUGHT IRON GATES

STOR

BENCH

D W

LINEN

GARAGE
25/0 X 22/0

91'

63'

Featuring

iLevel

Trus Joist · Structurwood · Weyerhaeuser

Plan L02-1235
The Broderick

Total Area 2,999 Sq. Ft.

Included Foundation *Crawlspace*

Spacious, one-level living has arrived. This contemporary home features a three-car garage, front and back patios, plenty of bookcases and shelving, media storage space, a niche off the den and much more. Separated by the great room and kitchen/dining area, the sectioned-off master suite, den, and additional bedrooms all feel like individual flats.

Floor plan labels

PATIO

DINING
13/6 X 15/0 +/-
(10' CLG.)

MASTER
17/2 X 15/0 +
(10' CLG.)

BUILT-IN

BR. 3
14/8 X 12/4 +
(10' CLG.)

GREAT RM.
21/0 X 23/0
(13'-4" CLG.)

MEDIA

BK.CASES

BUILT-IN

M/W

SHLVS

(10' CLG.)

REF
DESK
13/6 X 18/4 +/-
(10' CLG.)

BR. 2
12/10 X 14/4 +
(10' CLG.)

PAN

W/D

NICHE

(10' CLG.)

LINEN

PATIO

DEN
12/0 X 12/4 +
(10' CLG.)

99'

77'

GARAGE
26/0 X 22/6 +

22/0 X 12/0 +

Featuring
iLevel™
Trus Joist · Structurwood · Weyerhaeuser

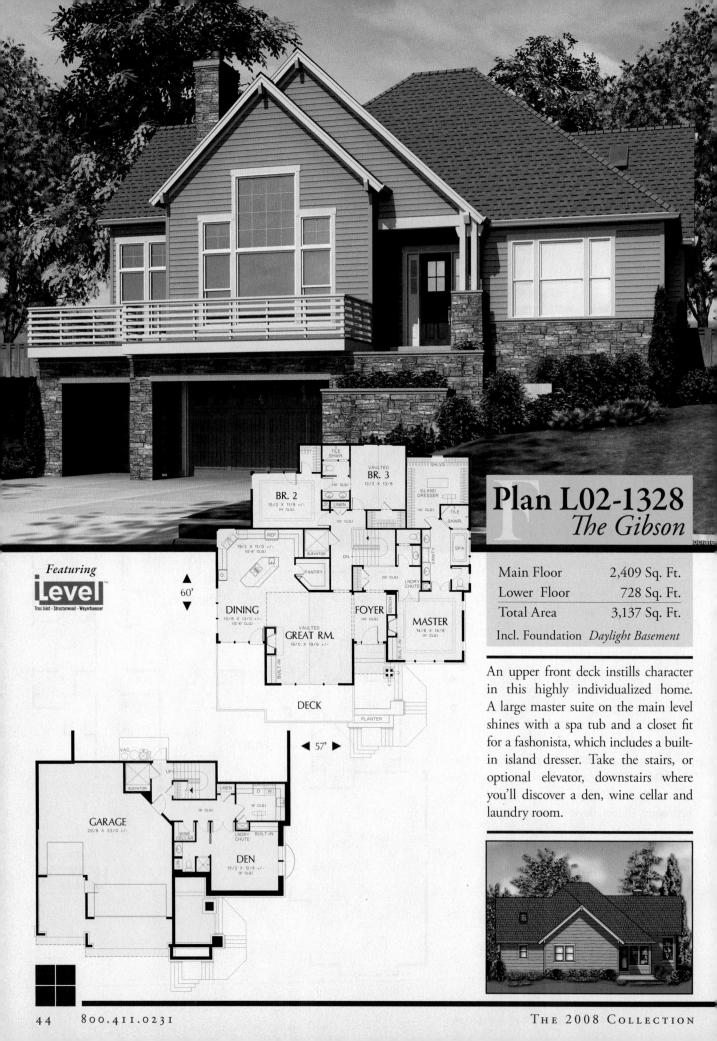

Plan L02-1328
The Gibson

Featuring
iLevel
Trus Joist · Structurwood · Weyerhaeuser

▲
60'
▼

TILE SHWR
VAULTED
BR. 3
12/2 X 13/8
(10' CLG.)

SHLVS

BR. 2
15/2 X 11/8 +/-
(11' CLG.)

LINEN

ISLAND DRESSER

(10' CLG.)

TILE SHWR.

REF
19/2 X 11/0
(12'-6" +/-)

ELEVATOR

PANTRY

DN.

(10' CLG.)

VANITY

SPA

LNDRY CHUTE

DINING
10/6 X 13/0 +/-
(12'-6" +/-)

VAULTED
GREAT RM.
19/0 X 19/6 +/-

FOYER
(10' CLG.)

BENCH

BUILT-IN

MASTER
14/6 X 14/8
(11' CLG.)

BUILT-IN

DECK

PLANTER

◄ 57' ►

VAC.

UP

ELEVATOR

LINEN

(9' CLG.)

D [W]

(9' CLG.)

GARAGE
29/8 X 33/0 +/-

WINE CELLAR

LNDRY CHUTE

BUILT-IN

DEN
15/2 X 12/8
(9' CLG.)

Main Floor	2,409 Sq. Ft.
Lower Floor	728 Sq. Ft.
Total Area	3,137 Sq. Ft.

Incl. Foundation *Daylight Basement*

An upper front deck instills character in this highly individualized home. A large master suite on the main level shines with a spa tub and a closet fit for a fashonista, which includes a built-in island dresser. Take the stairs, or optional elevator, downstairs where you'll discover a den, wine cellar and laundry room.

Plan L02-1413
The Lambert

Main Floor	2,679 Sq. Ft.
Lower Floor	1,654 Sq. Ft.
Total Area	4,333 Sq. Ft.
Mech/Storage	+312 Sq. Ft.

Incl. Foundation *Daylight Basement*

Highly livable and lavishly comfortable, this contemporary home features enough room for the entire family. With rooms designed to relax, create and entertain, this home features a separated office off the foyer, a game room, an airy sunroom, a front porch and a back deck.

Featuring

iLevel
Trus Joist · Structurwood · Weyerhaeuser

DECK

GREAT RM.
VAULTED
17/0 X 23/2

MASTER
14/2 X 16/2
(10' CLG.)

KIT/NOOK
23/0 X 17/0 +/-
(9' CLG.)

SUN RM.
15/0 X 14/0
(9' CLG.)

DINING
11/0 X 16/8
(9' CLG.)

FOYER
(9' CLG.)

OFFICE
11/8 X 12/2 + BAY
(9' CLG.)

PORCH

GARAGE
22/0 X 37/6 +/-

◄ 75' ►

87'

MEDIA
10/6 X 12/8
(10' CLG.)

GAMES RM.
17/0 X 21/6
(10' CLG.)

BR. 2
12/2 X 13/10
(10' CLG.)

BR. 3
10/10 X 15/2

MECH/STOR
13/6 X 17/10
(10' CLG.)

EXTENT OF SLAB

CRAWLSPACE

Plan L02-22122T
The Sophia

Upper Floor	655 Sq. Ft.
Lower Floor	1,746 Sq. Ft.
Sub-Total	2,401 Sq. Ft.
Bonus Room	+496 Sq. Ft.
Included Foundation	*Crawlspace*

A Tudor-style home created with both beauty and functionality in mind — this four-bedroom home boasts a lofted second level with two bedrooms and a large bonus room. Below: the great room, foyer and master bedroom all feature vaulted ceilings. A shop off the garage continues to balance this home's splendid beauty with a focus on utility.

Featuring
iLevel™
Trus Joist · Structurwood · Weyerhaeuser

BR. 2
10/0 X 12/2 +/-

OPEN TO BELOW

LINEN

BONUS
20/2 X 23/2 +/-

LOFT
BKSHLVS   BKSHLVS

OPEN TO BELOW

DN.

BR. 3
10/6 X 12/0 +

ATTIC STORAGE

VAULTED MASTER
13/6 X 16/6

SPA

9' CLG.

NOOK
10/2 X 12/6
(9' CLG.)

SHELVS

VAULTED GREAT RM.
17/6 X 17/10

PAN

REF

SHOP
11/0 X 9/6

56'

UP

9' CLG.

STORAGE

GARAGE
20/0 X 19/6

BUILT-INS

VAULTED FOYER

DEN/BR. 4
11/0 X 10/6
(9' CLG.)

BLT-INS

DINING
10/6 X 13/0
(9' CLG.)

◀ 50' ▶

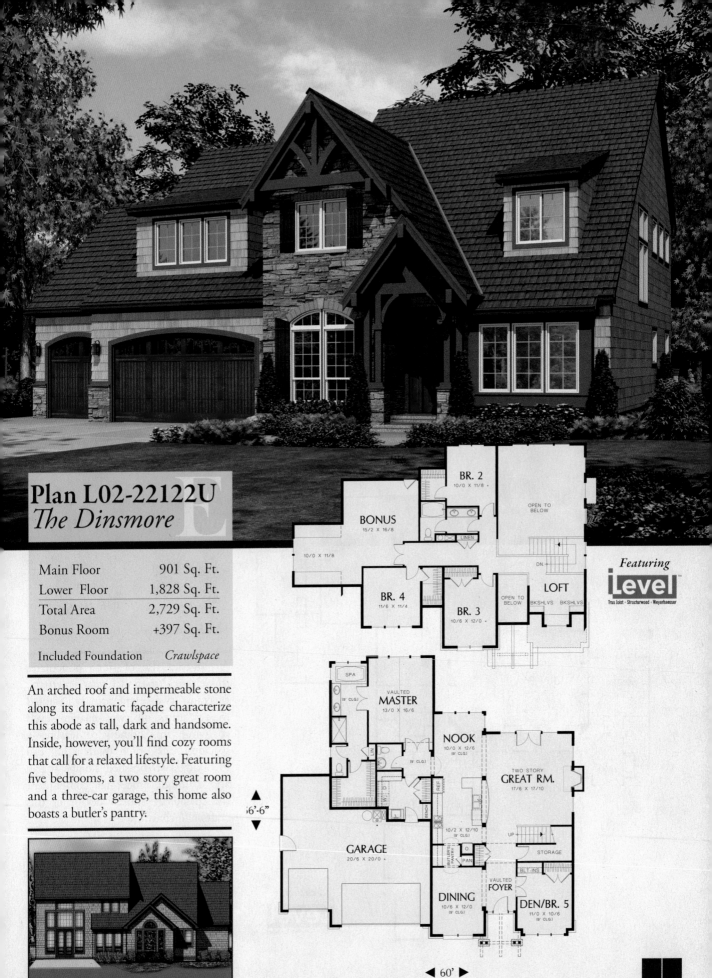

Plan L02-22122U
The Dinsmore E

Main Floor	901 Sq. Ft.
Lower Floor	1,828 Sq. Ft.
Total Area	2,729 Sq. Ft.
Bonus Room	+397 Sq. Ft.
Included Foundation	*Crawlspace*

An arched roof and impermeable stone along its dramatic façade characterize this abode as tall, dark and handsome. Inside, however, you'll find cozy rooms that call for a relaxed lifestyle. Featuring five bedrooms, a two story great room and a three-car garage, this home also boasts a butler's pantry.

Featuring
iLevel™
Trus Joist · Structurwood · Weyerhaeuser

Floor plan labels:

BR. 2 — 10/0 X 11/8
BONUS — 15/2 X 16/8
10/0 X 11/8
LINEN
OPEN TO BELOW
BR. 4 — 11/6 X 11/4
BR. 3 — 10/6 X 12/0
OPEN TO BELOW
LOFT — BKSHLVS BKSHLVS
DN

SPA
VAULTED MASTER — 13/0 X 16/6
(9' CLG.)
NOOK — 10/0 X 12/6 (9' CLG.)
TWO STORY GREAT RM. — 17/6 X 17/10
REF
10/2 X 12/10 (9' CLG.)
UP
STORAGE
GARAGE — 20/6 X 20/0 +
BUTLER'S PANTRY
PAN
BLT-INS
VAULTED FOYER
DINING — 10/6 X 12/0 (9' CLG.)
DEN/BR. 5 — 11/0 X 10/6 (9' CLG.)

66'-6"
60'

Plan L02-2461
The Dennison

Upper Floor	1,439 Sq. Ft.
Main Floor	2,879 Sq. Ft.
Total Area	4,318 Sq. Ft.
Included Foundation	*Crawlspace*

A gorgeous use of stone punctuates this classic Arts and Crafts sanctuary. Boasting two extraordinary, vaulted master suites on two separate levels of living, this home also features a spacious back porch (with a hot tub to boot). Two finished storage spaces and a unique office area compliment the splendidly chosen details of this craftsman charmer.

Featuring
iLevel
Trus Joist · Structurwood · Weyerhaeuser

Plan L02-2389
The Raymond

Upper Floor	1,522 Sq. Ft.
Main Floor	1,685 Sq. Ft.
Lower Floor	208 Sq. Ft.
Total Area	3,415 Sq. Ft.

Incl. Foundation *Daylight Basement*

With three levels, rectangular lines and oversized windows, this modern home offers unparalleled vantage points from which to see the day. Particularly innovative details include: a closed-in entertaining deck off the dining area, an elevator and a wall of windows throughout.

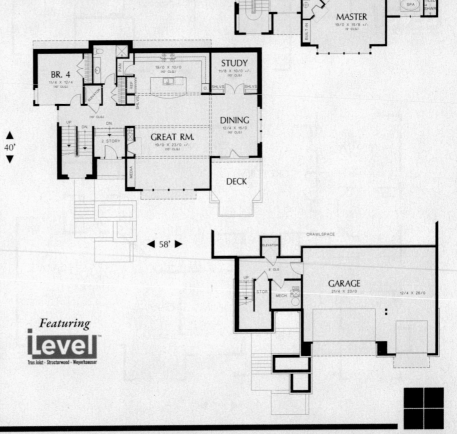

Featuring
iLevel™
Trus Joist · Structurwood · Weyerhaeuser

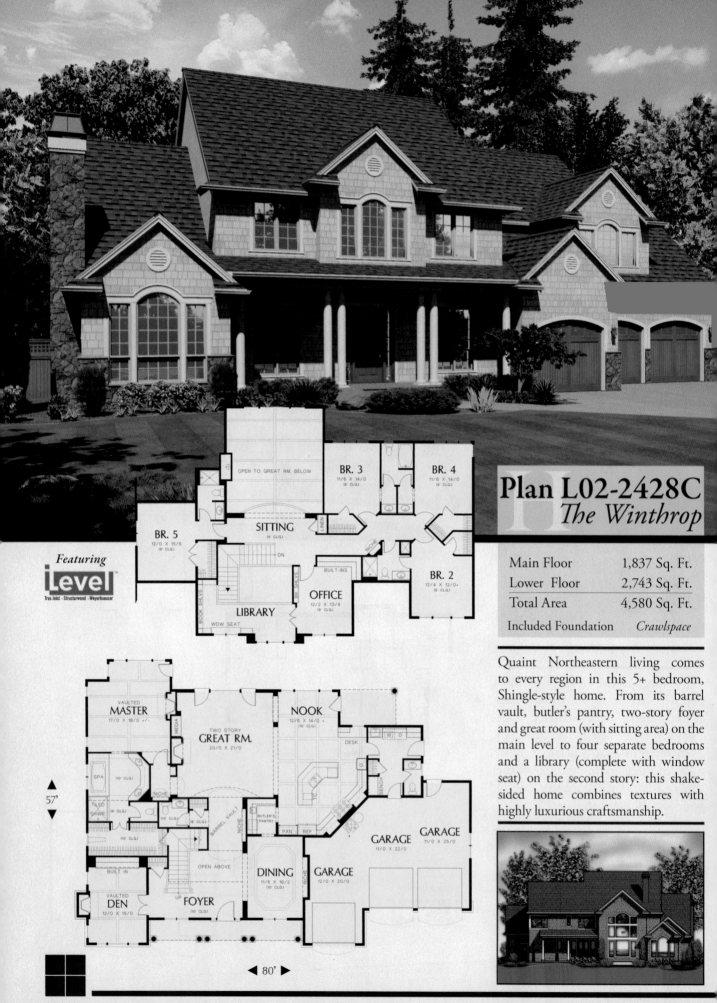

Plan L02-2428C
The Winthrop

Main Floor	1,837 Sq. Ft.
Lower Floor	2,743 Sq. Ft.
Total Area	4,580 Sq. Ft.
Included Foundation	*Crawlspace*

Quaint Northeastern living comes to every region in this 5+ bedroom, Shingle-style home. From its barrel vault, butler's pantry, two-story foyer and great room (with sitting area) on the main level to four separate bedrooms and a library (complete with window seat) on the second story: this shake-sided home combines textures with highly luxurious craftsmanship.

Featuring
iLevel
Trus Joist · Structurwood · Weyerhaeuser

Second Floor labels:
BR. 3 — 11/6 X 14/0 (9' CLG.)
BR. 4 — 11/8 X 14/0 (9' CLG.)
BR. 5 — 12/0 X 15/6 (9' CLG.)
SITTING (9' CLG.)
OPEN TO GREAT RM. BELOW
LINEN
NICHE
DN.
BR. 2 — 12/4 X 12/0 (9' CLG.)
BUILT-INS
OFFICE — 12/2 X 13/4 (9' CLG.)
LIBRARY
BOOK SHLVS
BK SHLVS
WDW SEAT

Main Floor labels:
VAULTED MASTER — 17/0 X 18/0 +/-
GREAT RM. — TWO STORY — 20/0 X 21/0
NOOK — 12/6 X 14/0 (10' CLG.)
DESK
SPA
NICHE (9' CLG.)
W.C. (10' CLG.)
SHWR
(10' CLG.)
(10' CLG.)
BARREL VAULT
NICHE
BUTLER'S PANTRY
PAN. REF
W
BENCH
GARAGE — 11/0 X 22/0
GARAGE — 11/0 X 25/0
GARAGE — 12/0 X 20/0
OPEN ABOVE
DINING — 11/6 X 16/2 (10' CLG.)
NICHE
BUILT IN
VAULTED DEN — 12/0 X 15/0
UP FOYER (10' CLG.)
MEDIA

57'

80'

Plan L02-2460
The Aberle

Upper Floor	1,934 Sq. Ft.
Main Floor	2,194 Sq. Ft.
Total Area	4,128 Sq. Ft.
Included Foundation	*Crawlspace*

A sweeping entry creates awestruck street appeal in this two-story, estate-like home. Featuring a versatile first level, complete with a private den and a bedroom: upstairs you'll find two additional bedrooms, the master suite, a library and a bonus/game room. Shelving and built-in storage along the staircase allow for individualized style and encourage an optimal use of space.

Featuring
iLevel
Trus Joist · Structurwood · Weyerhaeuser

DECK

BR. 2
13/0 X 14/8
(10' CLG.)

MASTER BR.
19/0 X 17/6
(10' CLG.)

SPA

TILED SHWR

LINEN

PLANT SHELF

GAMES RM.
14/0 X 18/2
(10' CLG.)

BR. 3
13/6 X 11/6
(10' CLG.)

LIBRARY
7/0 X 16/0
(10' CLG.)

DN.

PLANT SHELF

NOOK
11/0 X 12/6
(10' CLG.)

BR. 4
14/8 X 13/6
(10' CLG.)

14/6 X 14/6 +/-
(10' CLG.)

GREAT RM.
22/0 X 18/6
(10' CLG.)

PAN.

REF.

BUILT-IN

MEDIA

UP.

DINING
14/0 X 12/0 +/-
(10' CLG.)

7/0 X 16/0
(10' CLG.)

STORAGE

BKSHLVS.

DEN
13/0 X 12/0 +
(10' CLG.)

NICHE

92'

14/0 X 5/0

GARAGE
21/0 X 33/0

15/0 X 5/0

RETAINING WALL

◄ 55' ►

Plan L02-22169
The Somerset

Upper Floor	1,077 Sq. Ft.
Main Floor	1,364 Sq. Ft.
Total Area	2,441 Sq. Ft.
Included Foundation	*Crawlspace*

High-end architectural finishes and a focus on outdoor living space distinguish this flexible four-bedroom home. Built for its residents to entertain and unwind, The Somerset boasts a vaulted ceiling (in the great room), a spa tub complete with niche (in the master bath) and a unique, detached garage with covered walkway.

GARAGE
19/0 X 21/0

©Alan Mascord Design Associates, Inc.

SPA
NICHE
TILED SHWR
BR. 3
12/0 X 11/0
BR. 2
10/6 X 14/8
DN.
LIN
LIN
NICHE
MASTER BR.
VAULTED
16/0 X 13/6
©Alan Mascord Design Associates, Inc.
SHLVS
GREAT RM. BELOW

72'

9/8 X 9/6
(9' CLG.)
STOR
UP
REF
14/2 X 13/8 +/-
(9' CLG.)
(8' CLG.)
BRM
PANTRY
DESK
(8' CLG.)
DINING
14/0 X 12/0 •
(9' CLG.)
DEN/BR.4
12/4 X 11/0
(9' CLG.)
FOYER
9/0 X 13/0
(9' CLG.)
GREAT RM.
VAULTED
19/0 X 17/0 •

◄ 44' ►

Featuring
iLevel™
Trus Joist · Structurwood · Weyerhaeuser

Plan L02-2390
The Hamilton

Upper Floor	1,114 Sq. Ft.
Main Floor	2,486 Sq. Ft.
Sub Total	3,600 Sq. Ft.
Bonus Room	+406 Sq. Ft.

Included Foundation	*Crawlspace*

In a class of its own, this indulgently spacious 4+ bedroom home brings the comfort of an estate to the neighborhood of your choice. A second floor balcony (off the front-facing bonus room) recalls Parisian grace, which continues throughout the home. Additional features include a sweeping back porch.

Featuring
iLevel
Trus Joist · Structurwood · Weyerhaeuser

BR. 2
13/0 X 16/2

BR. 3
11/4 X 12/0

BR. 4
11/4 X 12/0

VAULTED FOYER

DN.

PLANT SHELF

VAULTED BONUS
17/9 X 23/9 +/-

SPA

BALCONY

NOOK
9/8 X 13/0

PORCH

DEN
12/6 X 15/6

VAULTED MASTER
16/0 X 14/6

VAULTED GREAT RM.
17/6 X 21/6

MEDIA

SEAT

NICHE

LINEN

VAULTED FOYER

UP

STOR

SHLVS

SHELVES

PANTRY

FRZR

VAULTED DINING
11/0 X 15/2

STORAGE ISLAND

BENCH

83'

66'-6"

GARAGE
23/6 X 32/6

Plan L02-1329A
The Langley G

Main Floor	2,145 Sq. Ft.
Lower Floor	1,413 Sq. Ft.
Total Area	3,558 Sq. Ft.

Incl. Foundation *Daylight Basement*

A traditional exterior endowed with exceptional, arch-inspired design encapsulates this home's combination of superior architecture and livability. An expansive outdoor living space off the oversized great room, a large game room/bonus space downstairs and three bedrooms (with an optional fourth, or den) are chock-full with built-ins yet maintain plenty of unobstructed space.

OUTDOOR LIVING
23/0 X 13/6 +/-
(11' CLG.)

NOOK
11/0 X 12/0
(9' CLG.)

MASTER
14/0 X 16/0
(10' CLG.)

GREAT RM.
22/0 X 20/0
(14' CLG.)

SPA

W D

REF
PAN

DINING
13/0 X 13/0
(11' CLG.)

FOYER
(11' CLG.)

GARAGE
19/0 X 21/6

DEN/BR 4
12/0 X 10/8
(9' CLG.)

BOOKS   BOOKS
SEAT

63'

◄ 60' ►

BR. 3
14/0 X 14/6
(9' CLG.)

BR. 2
11/4 X 15/0
(9' CLG.)

GAMES RM.
22/6 X 20/0
(9' CLG.)

MECH

STOR

DISPLAY
SNACK BAR   WINE   UP

Featuring
iLevel™
Trus Joist · Structurwood · Weyerhaeuser

Featuring
iLevel™
Trus Joist · Structorwood · Weyerhaeuser

©Alan Mascord Design Associates, Inc.

BR. 2
9/10 X 10/0

BR. 3
9/10 X 10/0

BR. 3
9/10 X 10/0

BR. 2
9/10 X 10/0

DN. | DN.

D | W | W | D

SHLVS | SHLVS

LIN | LIN

VAULTED
MASTER
11/0 X 12/0

VAULTED
MASTER
11/0 X 12/0

BENCH | BENCH

DINING
10/6 X 12/0 +/-
(9' CLG.)

DINING
10/6 X 12/0 +/-
(9' CLG.)

9/6 X 11/8 | 9/6 X 11/8
(9' CLG.) | (9' CLG.)

REF | REF

BLT-IN | BLT-IN

MEDIA | PAN | (8' CLG.) | (8' CLG.) | PAN | MEDIA

STOR | STOR

LIVING
14/8 X 13/8 +/-
(9' CLG.)

LIVING
14/8 X 13/8 +/-
(9' CLG.)

PLANTER BOX | PLANTER BOX

UP | UP

DECK | DECK

DN. TO
GRADE | DN. TO
GRADE

▲
41'
▼

◀ 21' ▶ ◀ 21' ▶

◀ 42' ▶

Plan L02-4027C
The Chelsea

Upper Floor	661 Sq. Ft.
Main Floor	695 Sq. Ft.
Total Area (Each Unit)	1,356 Sq. Ft.
Included Foundation	*Crawlspace*

18th Century brownstone charm pairs with the innovations of modern construction in these sublime and spacious two-story town homes. Closed-in front and back decks create perfect space to enjoy the outdoors year round while vaulted master bedrooms, and two additional bedrooms engender truly exquisite townhouse-style living.

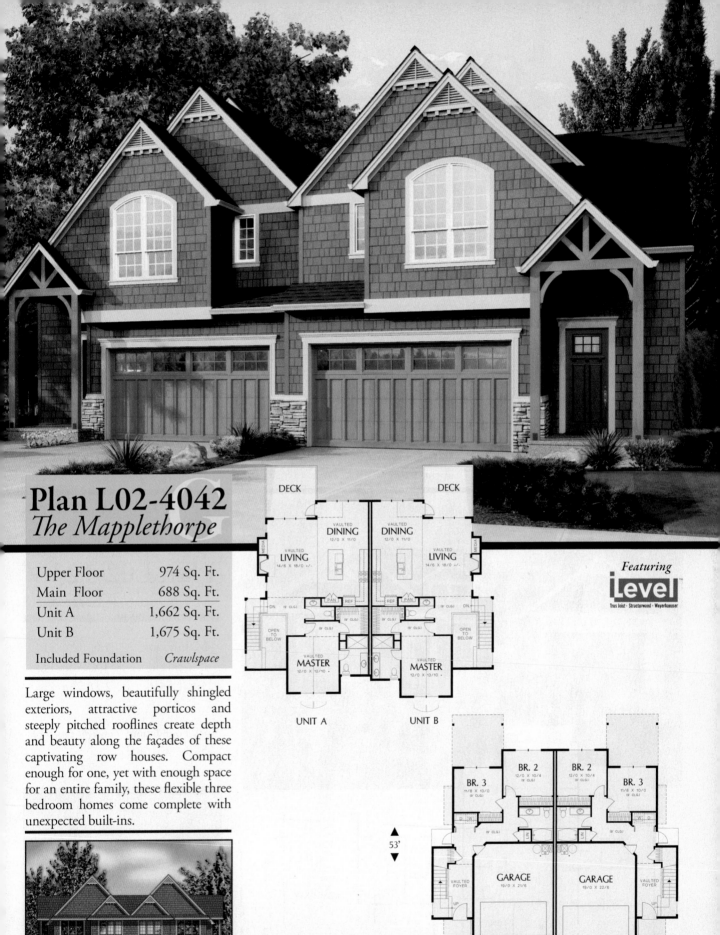

Plan L02-4042
The Mapplethorpe

Upper Floor	974 Sq. Ft.
Main Floor	688 Sq. Ft.
Unit A	1,662 Sq. Ft.
Unit B	1,675 Sq. Ft.
Included Foundation	*Crawlspace*

Large windows, beautifully shingled exteriors, attractive porticos and steeply pitched rooflines create depth and beauty along the façades of these captivating row houses. Compact enough for one, yet with enough space for an entire family, these flexible three bedroom homes come complete with unexpected built-ins.

DECK

DECK

VAULTED
DINING
12/0 X 11/0

VAULTED
DINING
12/0 X 11/0

VAULTED
LIVING
14/6 X 18/0 +/-

VAULTED
LIVING
14/6 X 18/0 +/-

MEDIA

MEDIA

PAN

REF

REF

PAN

DN.

DN.

OPEN
TO
BELOW

OPEN
TO
BELOW

VAULTED
MASTER
12/0 X 12/10

VAULTED
MASTER
12/0 X 13/10

UNIT A

UNIT B

Featuring

iLevel
Trus Joist • Structurwood • Weyerhaeuser

BR. 3
11/8 X 10/0

BR. 2
12/0 X 10/4

BR. 2
12/0 X 10/4

BR. 3
11/8 X 10/0

53'

VAULTED
FOYER

GARAGE
19/0 X 21/6

GARAGE
19/0 X 22/6

VAULTED
FOYER

UNIT A

UNIT B

30'

60'

30'

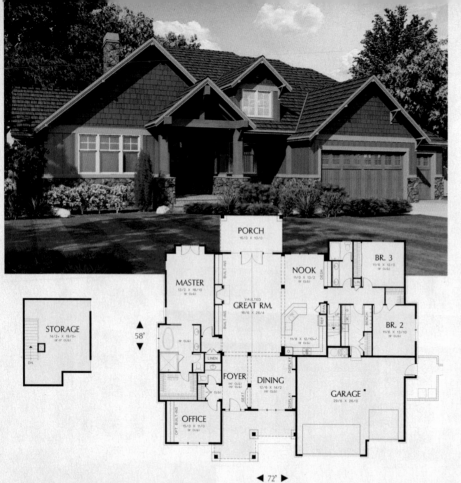

Plan L02-22157AA
The Ashby

Total Area	2,735 Sq. Ft.
Storage	+379 Sq. Ft.

Included Foundation *Crawlspace*

Plan L02-1236
The Linden

Main Floor	1,666 Sq. Ft.
Lower Floor	1,139 Sq. Ft.
Total Area	2,805 Sq. Ft.

Incl. Foundation *Daylight Basement*

Plan L02-1329
The Sycamore

Main Floor	2,152 Sq. Ft.
Lower Floor	1,413 Sq. Ft.
Total Area	3,565 Sq. Ft.

Incl. Foundation *Daylight Basement*

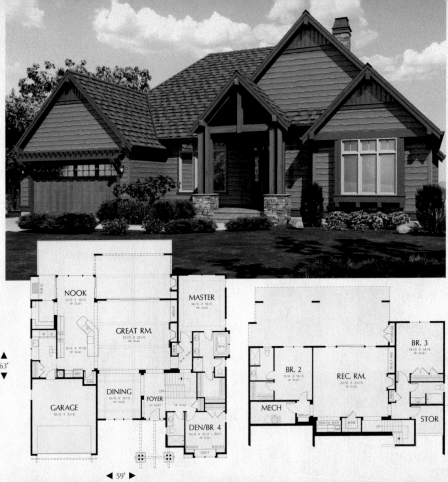

Plan L02-2391
The Berkshire

Upper Floor	1,598 Sq. Ft.
Main Floor	1,927 Sq. Ft.
Total Area	3,525 Sq. Ft.

Incl. Foundation *Crawlspace*

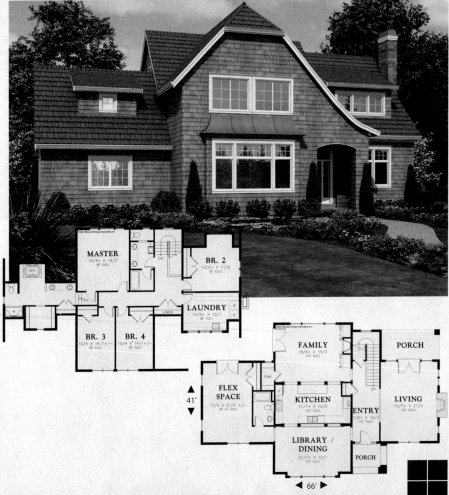

THE
CONTEMPORARY
COLLECTION

Our 2008 collection of fresh, completely livable contemporary home plans makes modern living easier and more handsome than ever before. Large windows, open spaces, the latest innovations in construction and a wide use of materials help instill each contemporary home with its own unique style. Whether looking to build a sleek, glass home of impressive proportions, a simple sanctuary with bold geometric shapes or an updated traditional home with attractively designed angles: the following selection of contemporary homes contains a diverse mix of features that will please even the most discriminating of modern home builders.

Our contemporary collection boasts homes designed around light and space — open, airy and with an abundance of windows in various styles, these homes are generously appointed to bring ample light indoors. Unique rooflines and asymmetrical designs create rooms that feel as grand as they are innovative. With a focus on maximizing square footage and minimizing costs, these pioneering modern homes are as reasonable to build as they are pleasant to live in.

Best of all, with various sizes and features to choose from, our 2008 collection of contemporary homes tailors modern style to your own individual tastes, which makes building one of our homes just as approachable as its modern-day design.

Photographs of more spectacular plans are available at
www.mascordlivingspaces.com

*Please note: Photographed homes may have been changed
to suit homeowner's preference*

PLAN L02-21113
Photography ©Bob Greenspan

Alumont
PLAN L02-21113

At first glance, this home's geometric shapes, intersecting angles and palette of warm and bright colors draw your attention, but its creative touches don't end with the playful architecture.

Personal residence of Design Director, Eric Schnell— this unique home is loaded with eco-friendly features and livable spaces.

Embedded in the cheerful outer façade are a number of energy-efficient and environmentally responsible features, the first of which is the house's correct solar orientation. Eric built the house to take advantage of the natural properties of the sun, with overhangs to block direct rays, and windows positioned to allow for proper ventilation. As for the roof, Schnell choose metal because it's more durable than asphalt or shingles and lasts longer, saving both building materials and money. It also allows the harvest of clean rainwater— for gardening or watering— that has not been contaminated with the chemical runoff from traditional roofing materials. The exterior employs fiber cement siding, composed of recycled concrete from post-industrial waste.

Inside, the main living space is open and airy— perfect for entertaining. A rich glow of copper & amber (from the stained concrete floor) blends beautifully with the décor and flows seamlessly from the entry to the great room. Once sealed, the concrete becomes non-porous, looks attractive and reduces the expense of additional flooring materials, such as carpet or tile. To keep the house and floor warm, Eric chose to use radiant heat, a system of piping embedded in the concrete floor that circulates hot water through heat sources while warming the floor through simple radiant heat.

The expansive kitchen, which seats four and opens to the great room, ensures no one is left out. The countertops are made from engineered quartz, an impenetrable material that is impervious to bacteria, unlike popular granite surfaces. It is also environmentally friendly made from rock dust replacing the limited resources of mined materials.

In the main bathroom, a mixture of recycled glass and concrete forms the countertop. The hardwood stairs leading to the second floor were sourced from a "farm forest", which plants and harvests trees in a cycle, creating a renewable resource.

Throughout this home, Eric made wise product choices from low-voltage light bulbs to low-flow showerheads, proving— you can live sustainable with style.

C *alumont*
PLAN L02-21113

Upper Floor	721 Sq. Ft.
Main Floor	1,178 Sq. Ft.
Total Area	1,899 Sq. Ft.
Incl. Foundation	*Crawlspace*

Please note: Photographed homes may have been changed to suit homeowners preference.

Norcutt
PLAN L02-1410

This ultra-contemporary hillside plan has some amazing details that add style to its appearance and comfort to its livability.

Extensive fenestration on the exterior takes advantage of ambient light on the inside. The upper level has a delightful entry foyer with stone columns, a bench and a niche. To the right is the open stairway to the lower level with a wall of windows on one side and a glass floor on the other. A wet bar connects the vaulted dining room to the professional-style kitchen (note the walk-in pantry). A vaulted nook with sliding doors to a patio is adjoining.

Step down into the vaulted great room, which also opens to the patio (note the outdoor grill and fireplace). A large, skylit laundry is close by. On the lower level you'll find a game room with built-in entertainment center, three family bedrooms, another laundry area and a snack-bar area.

The lower-level patio area is reached from Bedroom 2 or the game room. Don't miss the double garage with space for a shop.

THE CONTEMPORARY COLLECTION

H *Norcutt*
PLAN L02-1410

Main Floor	2,624 Sq. Ft.
Lower Floor	1,976 Sq. Ft.
Total Area	4,600 Sq. Ft.
Incl. Foundation	*Daylight Basement*

Please note: Photographed homes may have been changed to suit homeowners preference.

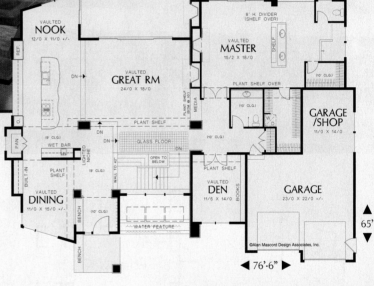

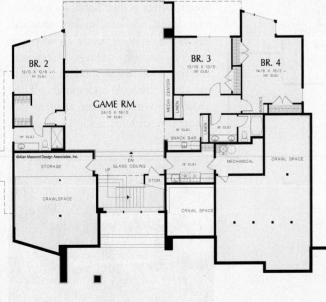

Plan L02-1327
The Mercer

Total Area	3,296 Sq. Ft.

Included Foundation	*Crawlspace*

This stunning, original contemporary home brings a chic sensibility to one level living. A long gallery separates the home's spaces, nearly all of which feature vaulted ceilings. Gorgeous, angular windows abound as do built-ins and niches. A back porch off the great room and master ensures that leisure time unfolds as seamlessly as this home's design.

Floor plan labels:

VAULTED NOOK 12/0 X 11/0 +/-
VAULTED GREAT RM 24/0 X 18/0
GAS GRILL
SPA
8' H. DIVIDER (SHELF OVER)
VAULTED MASTER 15/2 X 18/2
SHELF OVER
BUILT-IN DRESSER
SHELF
PLANT SHELF OVER
MEDIA
BR. 3 15/8 X 13/0 +/- (9' CLG.)
LINEN
GALLERY (10' CLG.)
WET BAR
LIGHTED NICHE
PLANT SHELF
OFFICE 13/2 X 12/0 + (9' CLG.)
PLANT SHELF OVER
NICHE
GARAGE 13/0 X 23/0
VAULTED DINING 11/0 X 15/0 +/-
BUILT-IN DESK
VAULTED BR. 2 12/0 X 15/8
BENCH
GARAGE 21/6 X 22/0
BENCH
STOR
PAN
REF
BUILT-IN
DN

65'
96'

Plan L02-22174
The Abbott

Upper Floor	523 Sq. Ft.
Main Floor	1,661 Sq. Ft.
Total Area	2,184 Sq. Ft.
Included Foundation	*Crawlspace*

An economical use of space and a truly singular design make this three-bedroom home the most distinctive property on nearly any block. A flat roof, simple lines and a combination of materials draw attention to the exterior. Interior highlights of this modern home include a master suite on the main, an office off the foyer and built-ins throughout.

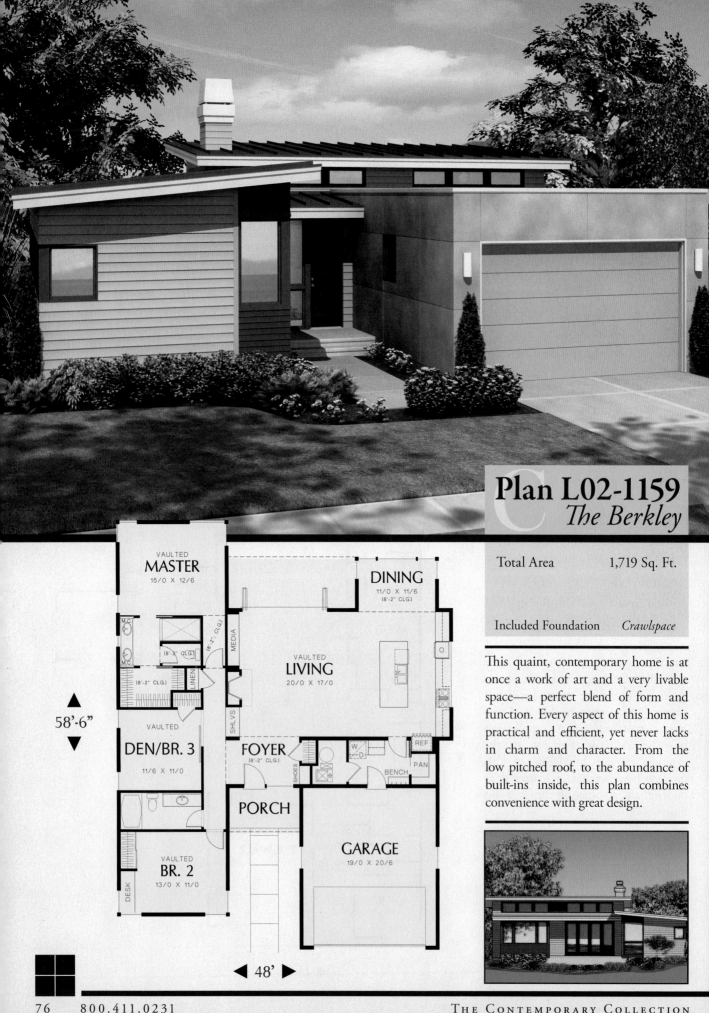

Plan L02-1159
The Berkley

Total Area	1,719 Sq. Ft.

Included Foundation	*Crawlspace*

This quaint, contemporary home is at once a work of art and a very livable space—a perfect blend of form and function. Every aspect of this home is practical and efficient, yet never lacks in charm and character. From the low pitched roof, to the abundance of built-ins inside, this plan combines convenience with great design.

Floor plan labels:

VAULTED
MASTER
15/0 X 12/6

DINING
11/0 X 11/6
(8'-2" CLG.)

(8'-2" CLG.)
(8'-2" CLG.)

M.C.
M.C.

MEDIA

VAULTED
LIVING
20/0 X 17/0

(8'-2" CLG.)

O.

LINEN

SHLVS

VAULTED

DEN/BR. 3
11/6 X 11/0

FOYER
(8'-2" CLG.)

SHOES

W. D.

REF

PAN

BENCH

58'-6"

VAULTED
BR. 2
13/0 X 11/0

DESK

PORCH

GARAGE
19/0 X 20/6

48'

Plan L02-21121
The Darbi

Upper Floor	903 Sq. Ft.
Main Floor	1,083 Sq. Ft.
Total Area	1,986 Sq. Ft.
Included Foundation	*Crawlspace*

Drawing inspiration from the designs of Frank Lloyd Wright, this contemporary plan takes prairie style to a new level. Natural stone accents blend with dramatic roof lines to create an exterior that is as sculptural as it is architectural. Inside, one moves freely from room to room in a plan that makes efficient use of square footage.

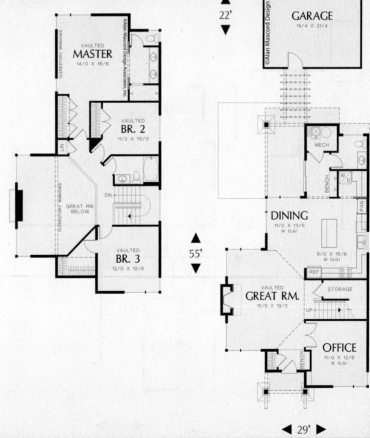

Plan L02-22180
The Eadin

MASTER
14/0 X 15/6

BR. 2
11/0 X 12/0

BR. 3
12/0 X 11/4

LINEN

PLANT SHELF OVER

DESK

DN

56'

DINING
12/0 X 13/8
(9'-2" CLG.)

LIVING
20/6 X 17/0
(12'-6" CLG.)

BUILT-INS

REF

O

DN

PAN

UP

MECH.

SHELVES

FOYER
(8'-2" CLG.)

GARAGE
19/0 X 23/0

OFFICE
12/0 X 12/10
(8'-2" CLG.)

◄ 40' ►

Upper Floor	1,038 Sq. Ft.
Main Floor	1,226 Sq. Ft.
Total Area	2,264 Sq. Ft.
Included Foundation	*Crawlspace*

This plan puts the "fun" back in functional, with a creative exterior that makes use of both wide and narrow siding. Inside, open living, dining, and kitchen areas make maximum use of the space, while an office is ideal spot for working from home or doing homework. 3 bedrooms upstairs make this a great plan for a growing family.

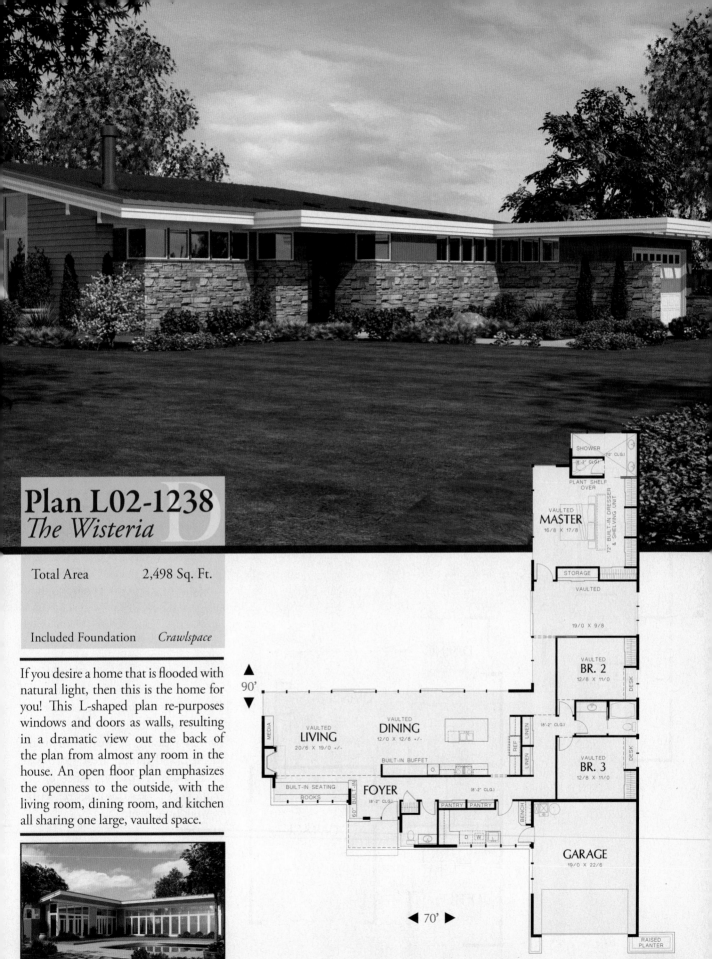

Plan L02-1238
The Wisteria

Total Area	2,498 Sq. Ft.

Included Foundation	*Crawlspace*

If you desire a home that is flooded with natural light, then this is the home for you! This L-shaped plan re-purposes windows and doors as walls, resulting in a dramatic view out the back of the plan from almost any room in the house. An open floor plan emphasizes the openness to the outside, with the living room, dining room, and kitchen all sharing one large, vaulted space.

Floor plan labels:

SHOWER
(8'-2" CLG.)
(12' CLG.)
PLANT SHELF OVER
VAULTED
MASTER
16/8 X 17/8
72" BUILT-IN DRESSER & SHELVING UNIT
STORAGE
VAULTED
19/0 X 9/8

VAULTED
BR. 2
12/8 X 11/0
DESK
(8'-2" CLG.)

VAULTED
BR. 3
12/8 X 11/0
DESK

90'

MEDIA
VAULTED
LIVING
20/6 X 19/0 +/-
VAULTED
DINING
12/0 X 12/8 +/-
REF
LINEN
LINEN
LINEN
BUILT-IN BUFFET
BUILT-IN SEATING
BOOKS
60" BUILT-IN
FOYER
(8'-2" CLG.)
(8'-2" CLG.)
PANTRY PANTRY
BENCH
D W

GARAGE
19/0 X 22/6

70'

RAISED PLANTER

Plan L02-22179
The Dain

VAULTED
MASTER
14/0 X 15/6

CLERESTORY WINDOWS

VAULTED
BR. 2
14/0 X 11/10

DN

DINING
12/0 X 12/8
(9'-2" CLG.)

LIVING
20/6 X 17/0
(12'-6" CLG.)

MEDIA

REF

DN

D W

PAN

UP

52'

MECH

SHELVES

GARAGE
19/0 X 23/0

OFFICE
12/0 X 11/10
(8'-2" CLG.)

BUILT-IN

◀ 40' ▶

Upper Floor	831 Sq. Ft.
Main Floor	1,216 Sq. Ft.
Total Area	2,047 Sq. Ft.
Included Foundation	*Crawlspace*

A creative mix of vertical and horizontal siding envelope the sleek contours of this home, resulting in an exterior that is pleasing to the eye. Inside, the floor plan is pleasing as well, with living, kitchen, and dining areas sharing an open space. A spacious office on the main floor makes this a perfect setting to work from home.

Plan L02-1330
The Cormac

Main Floor	1,893 Sq. Ft.
Lower Floor	1,349 Sq. Ft.
Total Area	3,242 Sq. Ft.

Incl. Foundation *Daylight Basement*

This contemporary home is a sight to admire on its own, but placed on a sloping lot it becomes even more magnificent! Mixed materials on the facade create a stunning exterior, while the inside is nothing short of unique. Large windows take advantage of the views out the back, and open onto large deck, truly bringing the outdoors in!

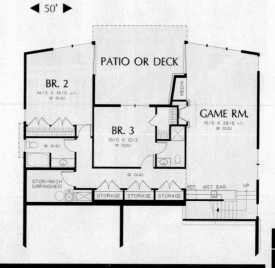

TRADITIONAL NEIGHBORHOOD DESIGN

A sense of community meets contemporary living in our 2008 traditional neighborhood design plans. Created specifically to complement one another, our traditional neighborhood design collection offers a mixture of plans, varying in size, shape and style. Taking their cues from America's most beloved small towns and villages, these timeless homes, appropriate for a variety of budgets and lifestyles, have been designed to foster quaint neighborhoods with visual continuity. From first time homebuyers and new families to singles and retirees: traditional neighborhoods accommodate a variety of lifestyles under the umbrella of a consistent architectural sensibility.

Our 2008 collection brings quality workmanship and elegance to the planned community. These plans foster a look all their own: a neighborhood of splendidly conceived homes that actually look like they belong side-by-side. In addition, the unifying architecture extends to the social climate of the neighborhood itself. On well-appointed porches, along narrow, quiet streets and in generous neighborhood squares, friends and neighbors become more accessible than ever. This means that socializing, a strong sense of safety and a comfortable, self-contained community can be counted as built-ins. With our 2008 plans, home designs work together just as seamlessly and self-sufficiently as the warmest small towns.

Photographs of more spectacular plans are available at
www.mascordlivingspaces.com

*Please note: Photographed homes may have been changed
to suit homeowner's preference*

SEABROOK, WA
Photography ©Bob Greenspan

Plan L02-22151A
The Dearborn

Upper Floor	1,390 Sq. Ft.
Main Floor	1,216 Sq. Ft.
Total Area	2,606 Sq. Ft.

Included Foundation   *Crawlspace*

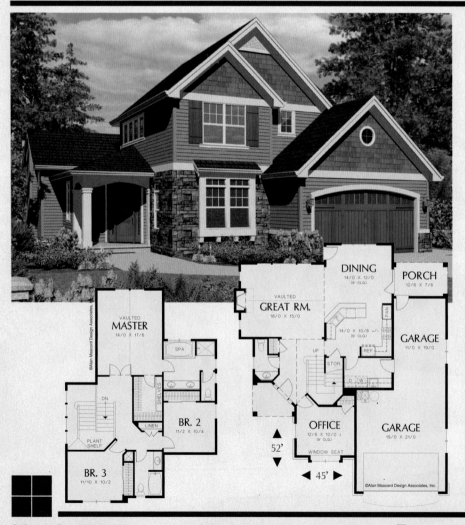

Plan L02-22138A
The Kenesaw

Upper Floor	970 Sq. Ft.
Main Floor	1,109 Sq. Ft.
Total Area	2,079 Sq. Ft.

Included Foundation   *Crawlspace*

Plan L02-22137F
The Mansfield

Upper Floor	1,571 Sq. Ft.
Main Floor	1,424 Sq. Ft.
Total Area	2,995 Sq. Ft.

Included Foundation *Crawlspace*

Plan L02-22155
The Gaylord

Upper Floor	1,335 Sq. Ft.
Main Floor	1,118 Sq. Ft.
Total Area	2,453 Sq. Ft.

Included Foundation *Crawlspace*

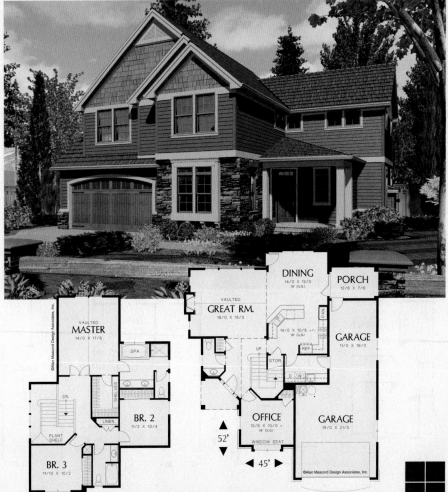

Plan L02-22153
The Norwood

Upper Floor	1,073 Sq. Ft.
Main Floor	1,205 Sq. Ft.
Total Area	2,278 Sq. Ft.

Included Foundation   *Crawlspace*

BR. 2
10/0 X 13/2

BR. 3
10/0 X 13/2

FOYER BELOW

DN.

LINEN

SPA

VAULTED
MASTER
13/0 X 18/0

©2005 Alan Mascord Design Associates, Inc.

6'-6"

NOOK
8/0 X 10/0
(8' CLG.)

GREAT RM.
19/0 X 17/6
(9' CLG.)

MEDIA CENTER

OFFICE
10/8 X 14/0
(9' CLG.)

11/0 X 12/0 +/-
(8' CLG.)

REF. PAN

2 STORY FOYER

STOR

GARAGE
19/0 X 20/6

DINING
10/0 X 12/0
(9' CLG.)

UP

©2005 Alan Mascord Design Associates, Inc.

42'

Plan L02-22154
The Fairfield

Upper Floor	1,463 Sq. Ft.
Main Floor	1,142 Sq. Ft.
Total Area	2,605 Sq. Ft.

Included Foundation   *Crawlspace*

©Alan Mascord Design Associates, Inc.

VAULTED
MASTER
17/8 X 12/6

OPTIONAL
GAMES RM.
15/0 X 15/0
(8' CLG.)

LINEN

BR. 2
10/6 X 16/0 +/-
(8' CLG.)

BENCH OR DRAWERS

LINEN

DN.

VAULTED

SPA

FOYER BELOW

VAULTED

BR. 3
14/0 X 11/0

SHOP
10/6 X 11/6

OFFICE
12/4 X 11/0
(9' CLG.)

MEDIA CENTER

GREAT RM.
15/0 X 17/6 +/-
(2 STORY OR OPT. 9' CLG.)

GARAGE
19/6 X 22/6

STOR

UP

DINING
11/6 X 14/0 +/-
(9' CLG.)

14/0 X 13/0
(9' CLG.)

REF

©Alan Mascord Design Associates, Inc.

42'

50'

Plan L02-22152A
The Morgan

Upper Floor	1,263 Sq. Ft.
Main Floor	1,215 Sq. Ft.
Total Area	2,478 Sq. Ft.

Included Foundation *Crawlspace*

Plan L02-22137EA
The Williston

Upper Floor	1,247 Sq. Ft.
Main Floor	1,255 Sq. Ft.
Sub Total	2,502 Sq. Ft.
Bonus Room	+295 Sq. Ft.

Included Foundation *Crawlspace*

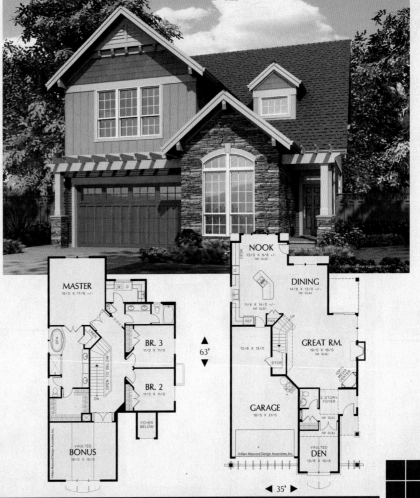

Plan L02-22154A
The Montgomery

Upper Floor	1,463 Sq. Ft.
Main Floor	1,142 Sq. Ft.
Total Area	2,605 Sq. Ft.

Included Foundation *Crawlspace*

A picturesque view of Thompson Meadows

Plan L02-22151
The Calhoun

Upper Floor	1,392 Sq. Ft.
Main Floor	1,226 Sq. Ft.
Total Area	2,618 Sq. Ft.

Included Foundation *Crawlspace*

Turn the page to see the Ashland Neighborhood...

Plan L02-2102AB
The Ansel

Upper Floor	990 Sq. Ft.
Main Floor	1,057 Sq. Ft.
Total Area	2,047 Sq. Ft.

Included Foundation *Crawlspace*

BR. 2
11/2 X 10/6+/-

BR. 3
10/6 X 11/10+

MASTER
15/6 X 12/0

VAULTED OFFICE
12/0 X 9/6

GARAGE
19/0 X 21/0

DINING
14/8 X 12/6+/-

GREAT RM.
15/6 X 18/6+/-

SHOP
10/0 X 10/6

42'-6"

47'

Plan L02-2137BC
The Adley

Upper Floor	1,059 Sq. Ft.
Main Floor	786 Sq. Ft.
Total Area	1,845 Sq. Ft.

Included Foundation *Crawlspace*

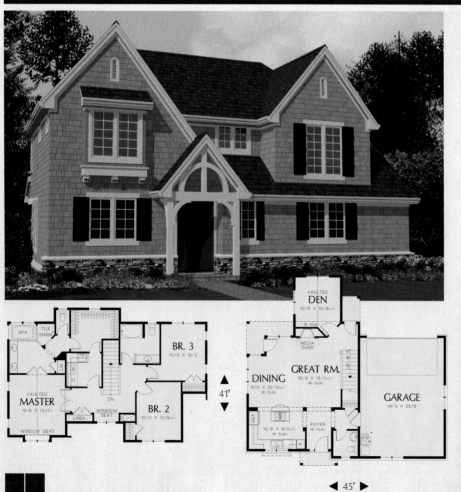

MASTER
12/6 X 13/0+/-

BR. 3
10/0 X 12/2

BR. 2
10/0 X 12/6+/-

VAULTED DEN
10/0 X 10/8+/-

DINING
9/0 X 10/10+/-

GREAT RM.
16/8 X 15/0+/-

GARAGE
19/0 X 25/6

41'

45'

Plan L02-22176
The Dakota

Upper Floor	1,052 Sq. Ft.
Main Floor	1,014 Sq. Ft.
Total Area	2,066 Sq. Ft.

Included Foundation *Crawlspace*

Plan L02-2102AC
The Barcley

Main Floor	911 Sq. Ft.
Lower Floor	1,065 Sq. Ft.
Total Area	1,976 Sq. Ft.

Included Foundation *Crawlspace*

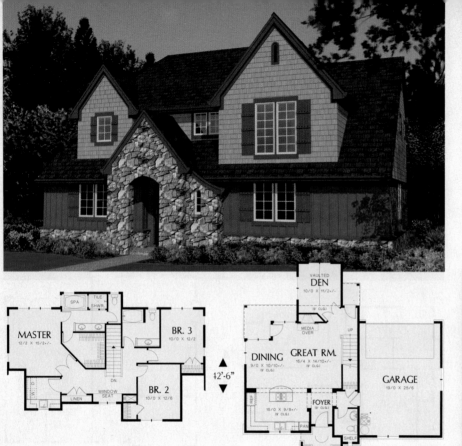

Plan L02-2137BB
The Watts

Upper Floor	1,051 Sq. Ft.
Main Floor	844 Sq. Ft.
Total Area	1,895 Sq. Ft.

Included Foundation *Crawlspace*

Plan L02-22176A
The Jackson

Upper Floor	1,044 Sq. Ft.
Main Floor	892 Sq. Ft.
Total Area	1,996 Sq. Ft.

Included Foundation *Crawlspace*

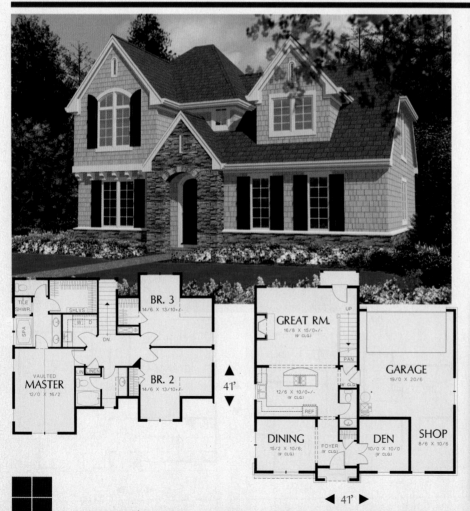

Plan L02-2102AD
The Hawthorne

Upper Floor	939 Sq. Ft.
Main Floor	988 Sq. Ft.
Total Area	1,927 Sq. Ft.

Included Foundation *Crawlspace*

Plan L02-2137BA
The Bailey

Upper Floor	1,028 Sq. Ft.
Main Floor	854 Sq. Ft.
Total Area	1,882 Sq. Ft.

Included Foundation *Crawlspace*

The Seabrook Community

Plan L02-21116A
The Elsie

Upper Floor	757 Sq. Ft.
Main Floor	932 Sq. Ft.
Total Area	1,689 Sq. Ft.
Included Foundation	*Crawlspace*

A covered entry, back porch, cedar siding and three spacious upstairs bedrooms add charm to this traditional home. Extras include a mudroom (with a built-in bench and adjacent half-bath) to an alcove in the eating nook.

BR. 2
10/4 X 11/8
(9' CLG.)

BR. 3
10/4 X 11/8
(9' CLG.)

MASTER
12/0 X 13/2
(9' CLG.)

COVERED PORCH

MUD RM.

W. D.

BENCH

10/10 X 11/0
(9' CLG.)

REF

NOOK
10/2 X 11/0
(9' CLG.)

ALCOVE

PANTRY

DESK

DINING
12/0 X 9/8
(9' CLG.)

LIVING
12/0 X 18/0
(9' CLG.)

UP

COVERED PORCH

©Alan Mascord Design Associates, Inc.

48'

22'

DN.

LN.

WH

Featuring

iLevel
Trus Joist · Structurwood · Weyerhaeuser

Plan L02-21118B
The Juniper

Upper Floor	661 Sq. Ft.
Main Floor	832 Sq. Ft.
Total Area	1,493 Sq. Ft.
Included Foundation	*Crawlspace*

A front porch recalls languid country evenings along the façade of this classic three bedroom home. With the warmth of this timeless farmhouse comes with built in modern amenities, including: a back mudroom with a built-in bench, a fully updated kitchen/dining area and a spacious living room complete with a fireplace.

BR. 2
10/4 X 12/0

BR. 3
10/4 X 12/0

DN

LIN

W.I.C.

MASTER
12/0 X 12/8

▲ 40′ ▼

D. W.

MUDROOM

BENCH

10/10 X 11/7
(9′ CLG.)

DINING
10/2 X 11/7
(9′ CLG.)

REF

DN FOR BSMT

PAN

DESK

LIVING
17/6 X 12/8
(9′ CLG.)

UP

©Alan Mascord Design Associates, Inc.

COVERED PORCH

◄ 22′ ►

Featuring
Level
Trus Joist · Structurwood · Weyerhaeuser

Plan L02-21115
The Osprey

Upper Floor	778 Sq. Ft.
Main Floor	1,096 Sq. Ft.
Total Area	1,874 Sq. Ft.
Included Foundation	*Crawlspace*

An enchanting wraparound front porch, spacious bedrooms, an additional media room and a generously appointed mudroom add delightful character to this three-bedroom charmer. A master on the main level, a fireplace in the living room and plenty of open space make this home irresistibly appropriate for both country and urban lifestyles.

Featuring

iLevel
Trus Joist · Structurwood · Weyerhaeuser

BR. 2
10/5 X 15/10
(9' CLG.)

BR. 3
10/5 X 15/10
(9' CLG.)

DESK

DN

MEDIA
15/7 X 9/5
(9' CLG.)

W. D. PAN
MUDROOM
BENCH

15/4 X 9/4
(9' CLG.)

MASTER
11/3 X 13/1
(9' CLG.)

REF

DINING
13/0 X 11/11
(9' CLG.)

43'

UP

LIVING
15/4 X 12/11
(9' CLG.)

COVERED PORCH

28'

TRADITIONAL NEIGHBORHOOD DESIGN

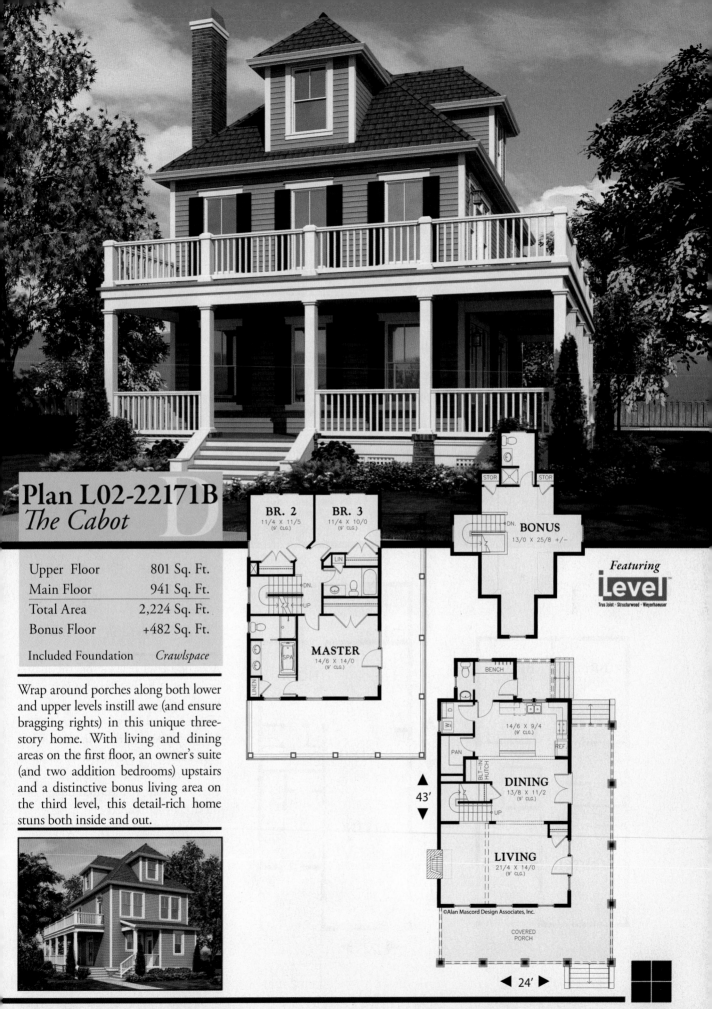

Plan L02-22171B
The Cabot

Upper Floor	801 Sq. Ft.
Main Floor	941 Sq. Ft.
Total Area	2,224 Sq. Ft.
Bonus Floor	+482 Sq. Ft.
Included Foundation	*Crawlspace*

Wrap around porches along both lower and upper levels instill awe (and ensure bragging rights) in this unique three-story home. With living and dining areas on the first floor, an owner's suite (and two addition bedrooms) upstairs and a distinctive bonus living area on the third level, this detail-rich home stuns both inside and out.

BR. 2
11/4 X 11/5
(9' CLG.)

BR. 3
11/4 X 10/0
(9' CLG.)

LIN

DN.

UP

MASTER
14/6 X 14/0
(9' CLG.)

SPA

LINEN

STOR

STOR

DN. **BONUS**
13/0 X 25/8 +/-

Featuring
iLevel™
Trus Joist · Structurwood · Weyerhaeuser

BENCH

14/6 X 9/4
(9' CLG.)

REF.

PAN

W D

BLT-IN
HUTCH

DINING
13/8 X 11/2
(9' CLG.)

UP

43'

LIVING
21/4 X 14/0
(9' CLG.)

©Alan Mascord Design Associates, Inc.

COVERED
PORCH

24'

Plan L02-21116B
The Ashville

Featuring
iLevel™
Trus Joist · Structorwood · Weyerhaeuser

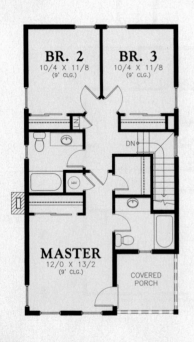

BR. 2	BR. 3
10/4 X 11/8	10/4 X 11/8
(9' CLG.)	(9' CLG.)

LN.

DN

MASTER
12/0 X 13/2
(9' CLG.)

COVERED PORCH

48'

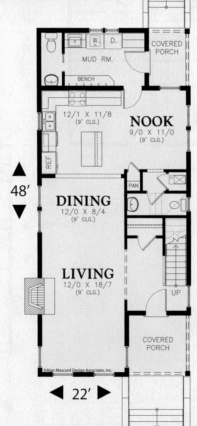

COVERED PORCH

MUD RM.

BENCH

W. | D.

12/1 X 11/8
(9' CLG.)

REF

NOOK
9/0 X 11/0
(9' CLG.)

PAN

DINING
12/0 X 8/4
(9' CLG.)

LIVING
12/0 X 18/7
(9' CLG.)

UP

COVERED PORCH

©Alan Mascord Design Associates, Inc.

22'

Upper Floor	757 Sq. Ft.
Main Floor	932Sq. Ft.
Total Area	1,689 Sq. Ft.
Included Foundation	*Crawlspace*

A second level balcony off the master bedroom, a back covered porch and a lovely eating nook make wonderful use of space in this two-story traditional home. Modern updates in the kitchen and a fantastic use of materials instill this three-bedroom home with the character and architectural design of a much statelier property.

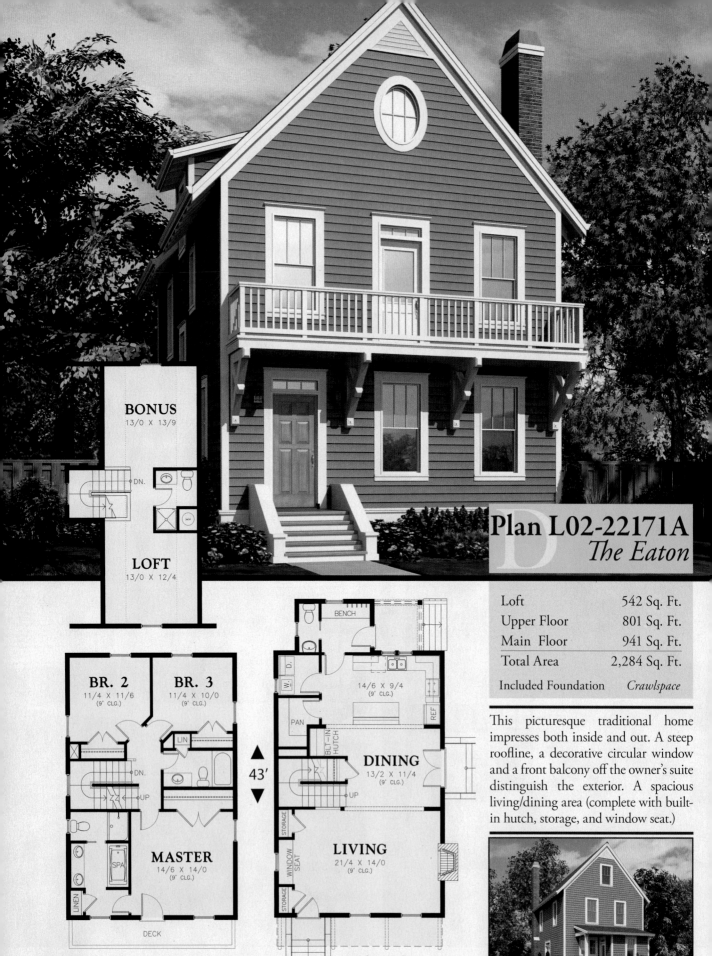

BONUS
13/0 X 13/9

LOFT
13/0 X 12/4

DN.

Plan L02-22171A
The Eaton

Loft	542 Sq. Ft.
Upper Floor	801 Sq. Ft.
Main Floor	941 Sq. Ft.
Total Area	2,284 Sq. Ft.
Included Foundation	*Crawlspace*

This picturesque traditional home impresses both inside and out. A steep roofline, a decorative circular window and a front balcony off the owner's suite distinguish the exterior. A spacious living/dining area (complete with built-in hutch, storage, and window seat.)

BR. 2
11/4 X 11/6
(9' CLG.)

BR. 3
11/4 X 10/0
(9' CLG.)

LIN

DN.

UP

MASTER
14/6 X 14/0
(9' CLG.)

SPA

LINEN

DECK

43'

BENCH

14/6 X 9/4
(9' CLG.)

W. D.

PAN

BLT-IN HUTCH

REF

DINING
13/2 X 11/4
(9' CLG.)

UP

STORAGE

WINDOW SEAT

STORAGE

LIVING
21/4 X 14/0
(9' CLG.)

24'

Plan L02-21118
The Mallory C

Upper Floor	658 Sq. Ft.
Main Floor	858 Sq. Ft.
Total Area	1,516 Sq. Ft.
Included Foundation	*Crawlspace*

From its gabled entry and wraparound, covered porch to abundant built-ins and updated amenities, this two-story, three bedroom home brings impeccable craftsmanship, thoughtful design and country-style living to the neighborhood. With particularly ample closet space and a built-in desk included off the pantry, this home meets and exceeds your daily storage needs.

Featuring
iLevel™
Trus Joist · Structurwood · Weyerhaeuser

BR. 2
10/4 X 12/0

BR. 3
10/4 X 12/0

LIN
LIN
DN

MASTER
12/0 X 12/8

DINING
10/2 X 11/7
(9' CLG.)

BENCH

10/10 X 11/7
(9' CLG.)

D. W.
REF

PAN
DESK

43'

LIVING
17/6 X 12/8
(9' CLG.)

UP

COVERED
PORCH

22'

Plan L02-21114
The Jasmine

Upper Floor	817 Sq. Ft.
Main Floor	1,079 Sq. Ft.
Total Area	1,896 Sq. Ft.

Included Foundation *Crawlspace*

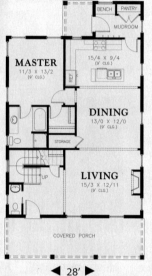

BR. 2
14/8 X 12/4

MEDIA RM.
15/5 X 12/6

BR. 3
14/0 X 9/6

MASTER
11/3 X 13/2
(9' CLG.)

BENCH PANTRY
MUDROOM

15/4 X 9/4
(9' CLG.)

DINING
13/0 X 12/0
(9' CLG.)

STORAGE

LIVING
15/3 X 12/11
(9' CLG.)

COVERED PORCH

43'

28'

Plan L02-22172D
The Hemingway

GAME ROOM
19/4 X 20/4 +/-

RAILING

Top Floor	705 Sq. Ft.
Upper Floor	901 Sq. Ft.
Main Floor	1,100 Sq. Ft.
Total Area	2,706 Sq. Ft.

Included Foundation *Crawlspace*

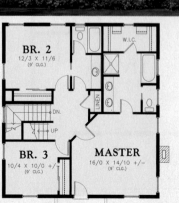

BR. 2
12/3 X 11/6
(9' CLG.)

W.I.C.

LINEN

BR. 3
10/4 X 10/0 +/-
(9' CLG.)

MASTER
16/0 X 14/10 +/-
(9' CLG.)

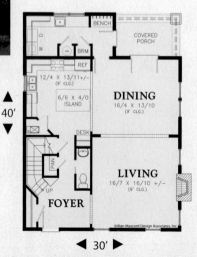

BENCH

W D

BRM

REF

COVERED PORCH

12/4 X 13/11+/-

6/6 X 4/0
ISLAND

DINING
16/4 X 13/10
(9' CLG.)

DESK

LIVING
16/7 X 16/10 +/-
(9' CLG.)

PAN

FOYER

©Alan Mascord Design Associates, Inc.

40'

30'

TRADITIONAL NEIGHBORHOOD DESIGN

Plan L02-22172B
The Fairfield

Top Floor	644 Sq. Ft.
Upper Floor	901 Sq. Ft.
Main Floor	1,100 Sq. Ft.
Total Area	2,645 Sq. Ft.

Included Foundation *Crawlspace*

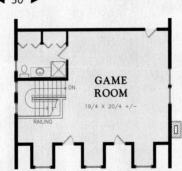

Plan L02-21117
The Newport

Upper Floor	803 Sq. Ft.
Main Floor	572 Sq. Ft.
Total Area	1,075 Sq. Ft.

Included Foundation *Crawlspace*

©Alan Mascord Design Associates, Inc.

BEST SELLING PLANS

Keeping abreast of the hottest national home trends has never been easier: our 2008 Best Sellers collection represents the most popular, inventive and time-tested home plans on the market. From affordable bungalows to stately homes suitable for the most discerning buyers, our 2008 Best Sellers collection impresses with proven sustainability and unmatched design. With an eclectic variation of home styles and architectural influences, the following homes are our most sought-after plans in their respective classes.

Up to date, artfully crafted, and proven to hold their value, our bestselling homes take full advantage of their square footage. With plenty of open space, flexible bonus rooms, large master suites and carefully chosen built-ins placed throughout, these homes are incredibly spacious, regardless of style or individual size. Move-up buyers, families, empty nesters, singles and couples all have reason to take delight in our collection of best selling homes, which feature award-winning designs that will compliment any lifestyle.

A perfect impetus for turning your fantasy home into a livable reality, our 2008 best seller collection features homes inspired by Traditional, Tudor, Cape Cod, Craftsman, Ranch, Modern, Colonial, Victorian architecture and more. Regardless of their particular influences, reviewing the remarkable craftsmanship, emphasis on economy, and splendid layout of each one of the following homes demonstrates why they collectively make up our 2008 set of best sellers.

Photographs of more spectacular plans are available at
www.mascordlivingspaces.com

*Please note: Photographed homes may have been changed
to suit homeowner's preference*

PLAN L02-2458
Photography ©Bob Greenspan

Granseth
PLAN L02-1320

Designed for hilly terrain, Granseth offers an open floor plan with lots of amenities.

Sloping lots are attractive in many ways, they often feature views, they allow good drainage, and they provide visual relief from flat areas.

The main floor is complete unto itself with a den, dining room, great room, nook, master suite and family bedroom. Special features to note: built-ins in the den; a fireplace, a scissor-vaulted ceiling, and a media center in the great room; sliding doors in the nook leading to a patio and deck; a built-in bookcase in Bedroom 2; a spa-like bath in the master suite.

Near the access to the three-car garage is a laundry room with plenty of linen storage. The lower level adds even more livability to the home: a games room with media center and corner fireplace, two more bedrooms (each with a full bath), and a wide covered patio.

Photography ©Bob Greenspan

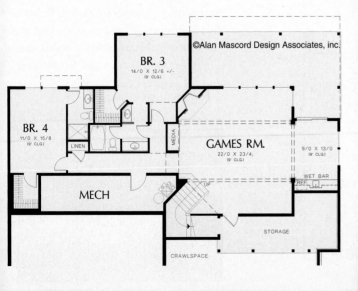

Granseth
PLAN L02-1320

Main Floor	2,192 Sq. Ft.
Lower Floor	1,490 Sq. Ft.
Total Area	3,682 Sq. Ft.

Included Foundation *Slab*

Please note: Photographed homes may have been changed to suit homeowners preference.

Featuring

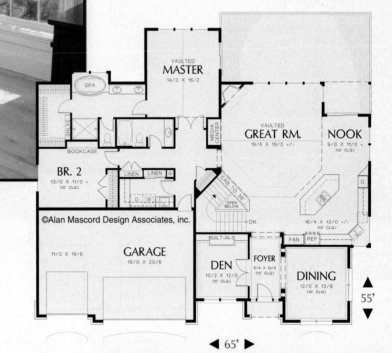

©Alan Mascord Design Associates, inc.

Plan L02-22134A
The Hannah

BR. 3
11/0 X 12/0

BR. 2
11/6 X 14/2

Upper Floor	471 Sq. Ft.
Main Floor	1,603 Sq. Ft.
Total Area	2,074 Sq. Ft.
Included Foundation	*Crawlspace*

Forget the comfortable livability of this plan (if you can)—it's just plain charming! A covered porch opens the way to interior spaces—a main level with living spaces and master suite, and an upper level with two family bedrooms. Designed for the way you live, the great room is vaulted and open to a dining area and handy kitchen.

Featuring
iLevel™
Trus Joist · Structurwood · Weyerhaeuser

VAULTED PORCH
12/0 X 8/0

DINING
11/6 X 13/8
(9' CLG.)

VAULTED GREAT RM.
17/0 X 18/8

VAULTED MASTER
13/8 X 15/6

10/4 x 14/2
(9' CLG.)

GARAGE /SHOP
10/0 X 15/0

VAULTED FOYER

OFFICE
10/6 X 14/2
(9' CLG.)

GARAGE
20/0 X 20/0

56'

50'

©Alan Mascord Design Associates, Inc.

114   800.411.0231

BEST SELLING PLANS

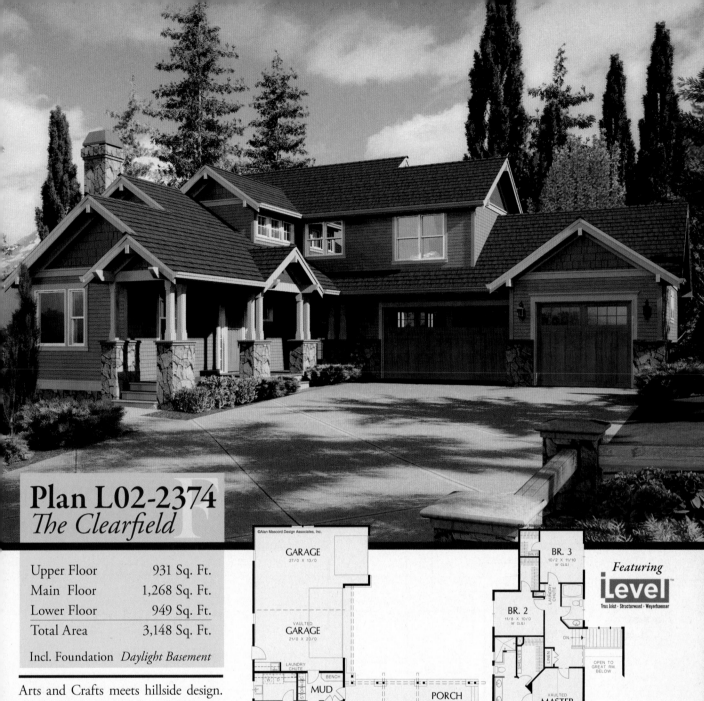

Plan L02-2374
The Clearfield

Upper Floor	931 Sq. Ft.
Main Floor	1,268 Sq. Ft.
Lower Floor	949 Sq. Ft.
Total Area	3,148 Sq. Ft.

Incl. Foundation *Daylight Basement*

Arts and Crafts meets hillside design. The result? A stunning design that perfectly fits a sloped site. Horizontal lap siding with stone and cedar shingle accents decorate the exterior. A covered porch introduces the front entry, but also allows access to a mudroom and the three-car garage beyond.

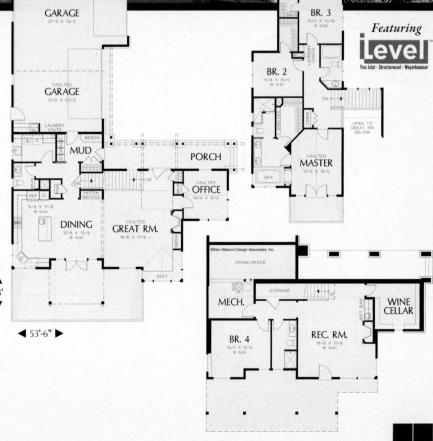

Plan L02-22128
The Kensington

Upper Floor	1,054 Sq. Ft.
Main Floor	1,464 Sq. Ft.
Sub-Total	2,518 Sq. Ft.
Bonus Room	+332 Sq. Ft.
Included Foundation	*Crawlspace*

The nearby kitchen contains gourmet appointments with an island countertop, a large pantry and a work desk. A formal dining room connects directly to the kitchen for convenience. A bedroom (or make it a home office) is tucked away behind the two-car garage and has the use of a full bath.

Featuring
iLevel
Trus Joist · Structurwood · Weyerhaeuser

Upper Floor Plan
- SPA
- MASTER 19/2 X 13/0 +
- OPEN TO BELOW
- ©Alan Mascord Design Associates, Inc.
- BONUS 11/0 X 23/0 +
- DN.
- LINEN
- BR. 3 11/0 X 12/0
- (8' CLG.)
- BR. 2 13/0 X 10/0; (10' CLG.)

Main Floor Plan
- NOOK 10/0 X 11/4 (9' CLG.)
- ©Alan Mascord Design Associates, Inc.
- BR. 4 13/0 X 11/0 (9' CLG.)
- 9/6 X 13/10 (9' CLG.)
- REF
- NICHE
- 2 STORY
- GREAT RM 19/0 X 15/0
- 12/10 X 11/0 +/-
- PAN
- DESK
- UP
- STOR
- GARAGE 21/0 X 19/6
- DINING 11/0 X 13/2 (9' CLG.)
- FOYER (9' CLG.)
- BUILT-INS
- DEN 10/5 X 13/3 +/- (9' CLG.)
- ALT GARAGE DR LOCATION
- 51'-6"
- 59'

Plan L02-2164A
The Malone

Upper Floor	871 Sq. Ft.
Main Floor	1,092 Sq. Ft.
Sub-Total	1,943 Sq. Ft.
Bonus Room	+356 Sq. Ft.
Included Foundation	*Crawlspace*

There are delightful surprises throughout this two-story home. A private study is furnished with handsome built-in storage. Impressive columns define the dining room. Upstairs, the master suite features a vaulted ceiling in the bedroom and a pampering bath.

Built by Macleod Construction
Photography by Mark Gossage

Featuring
iLevel™
Trus Joist · Structurwood · Weyerhaeuser

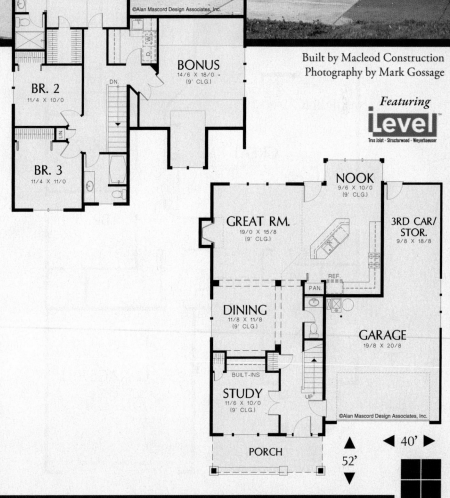

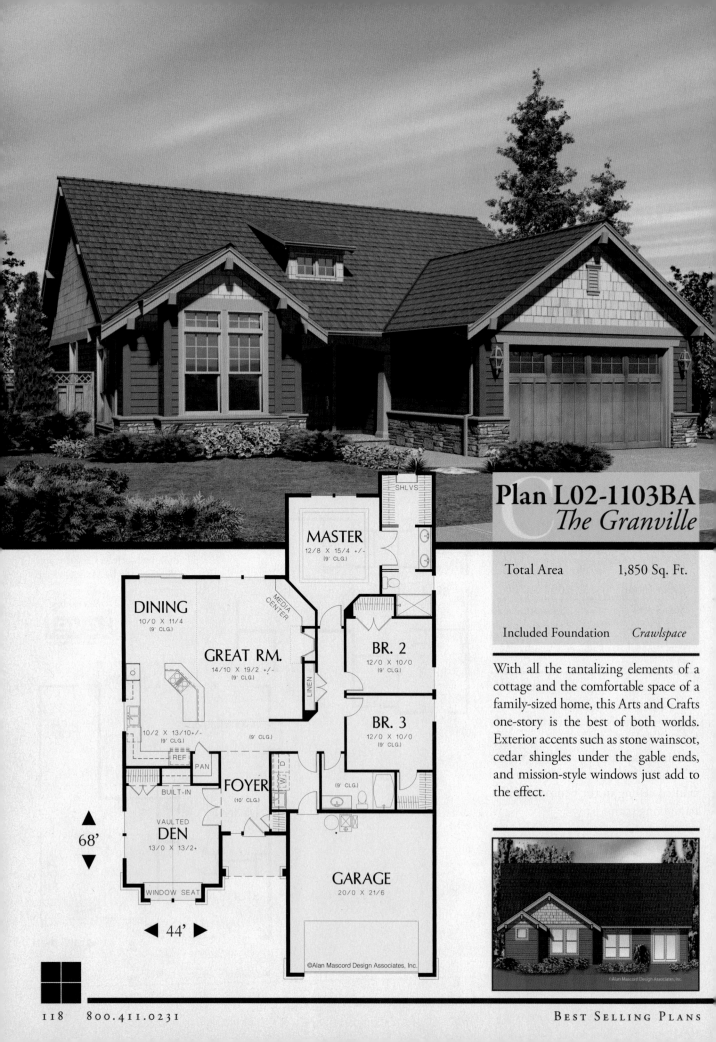

Plan L02-1103BA

The Granville

Total Area	1,850 Sq. Ft.

Included Foundation   *Crawlspace*

With all the tantalizing elements of a cottage and the comfortable space of a family-sized home, this Arts and Crafts one-story is the best of both worlds. Exterior accents such as stone wainscot, cedar shingles under the gable ends, and mission-style windows just add to the effect.

SHLVS

MASTER
12/8 X 15/4 +/-
(9' CLG.)

DINING
10/0 X 11/4
(9' CLG.)

MEDIA CENTER

GREAT RM.
14/10 X 19/2 +/-
(9' CLG.)

BR. 2
12/0 X 10/0
(9' CLG.)

LINEN

10/2 X 13/10+/-
(9' CLG.)

(9' CLG.)

BR. 3
12/0 X 10/0
(9' CLG.)

REF   PAN

FOYER
(10' CLG.)

(9' CLG.)

BUILT-IN

W D

VAULTED
DEN
13/0 X 13/2+

68'

GARAGE
20/0 X 21/6

WINDOW SEAT

44'

©Alan Mascord Design Associates, Inc.

Plan L02-2261H
The Camden

Upper Floor	1,181 Sq. Ft.
Main Floor	1,319 Sq. Ft.
Sub-Total	2,500 Sq. Ft.
Bonus Room	+371 Sq. Ft.
Included Foundation	*Crawlspace*

Symmetry is the order of the day in this plan. Cedar shingles and stone accents further the attraction. The floor plan is nicely designed, with formal living and dining areas flanking the foyer, and casual living to the back. A convenient butler's pantry connects the dining room and the service hall to the kitchen.

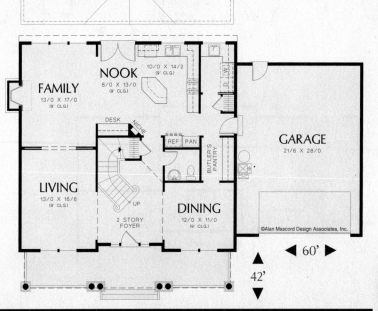

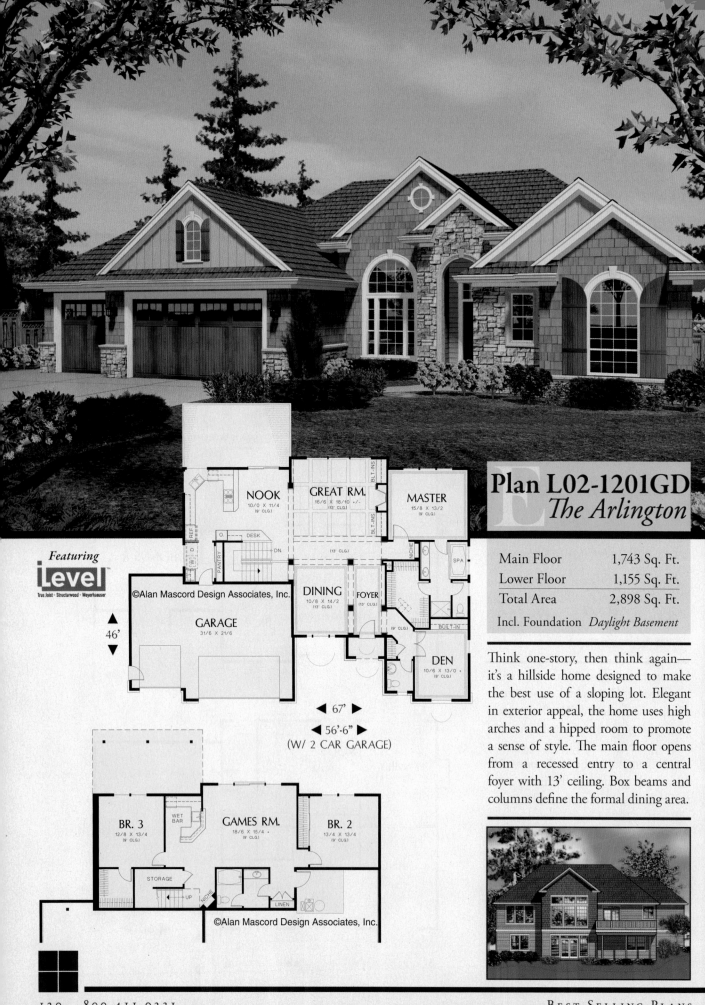

Plan L02-1201GD
The Arlington

Featuring
iLevel™
Trus Joist · Structurwood · Weyerhaeuser

©Alan Mascord Design Associates, Inc.

NOOK
10/0 X 11/4
[9' CLG.]

GREAT RM.
16/6 X 18/10 +/-
[9' CLG.]

MASTER
15/8 X 13/2
[9' CLG.]

REF

W.D

DESK

DN.

PANTRY

[13' CLG.]

NICHE

SPA

46'

GARAGE
31/6 X 21/6

DINING
10/8 X 14/2
[13' CLG.]

FOYER
[13' CLG.]

BUILT-IN

[9' CLG.]

DEN
10/6 X 13/0 +
[9' CLG.]

◄ 67' ►

◄ 56'-6" ►
(W/ 2 CAR GARAGE)

BR. 3
12/8 X 13/4
[9' CLG.]

WET
BAR

GAMES RM.
18/6 X 15/4 +
[9' CLG.]

BR. 2
13/4 X 13/4
[9' CLG.]

STORAGE

UP

NICHE

LINEN

©Alan Mascord Design Associates, Inc.

Main Floor	1,743 Sq. Ft.
Lower Floor	1,155 Sq. Ft.
Total Area	2,898 Sq. Ft.

Incl. Foundation *Daylight Basement*

Think one-story, then think again— it's a hillside home designed to make the best use of a sloping lot. Elegant in exterior appeal, the home uses high arches and a hipped room to promote a sense of style. The main floor opens from a recessed entry to a central foyer with 13' ceiling. Box beams and columns define the formal dining area.

Plan L02-22157A
The Ravenwood

Total Area	2,595 Sq. Ft.

Included Foundation	*Crawlspace*

Cedar shingles, vertical board-and-batten siding, ledgestone, and Doric columns come together in an eclectic mix on this home's elevation. The dining room offers built-in shelves, space for a hutch and a built-in seat. The open kitchen takes in views of the great room's fireplace and built-in media cabinets.

Featuring

iLevel™
Trus Joist · Structurwood · Weyerhaeuser

STORAGE
14/2 X 22/0+/-

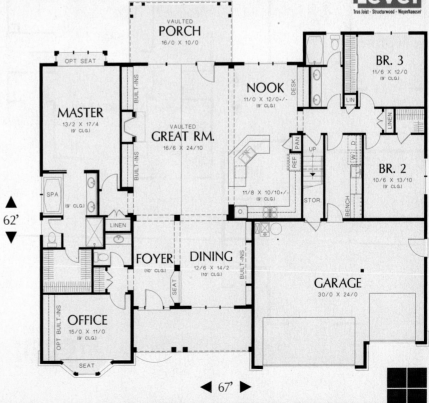

62'

67'

BR. 2
12/0 X 10/0
(9' CLG.)

BR. 3
12/0 X 10/8
(9' CLG.)

LOFT
14/2 X 7/0
(9' CLG.)

LINEN

DN.

NICHE

GREAT RM
BELOW

VAULTED
MASTER
14/0 X 16/0

©Alan Mascord Design Associates, Inc.

▲
40'
▼

©Alan Mascord Design Associates, Inc.

DINING
11/0 X 16/0
(9' CLG.)

12/6 X 12/6 +/-

NOOK
9/0 x 10/8 +/-
(9' CLG.)

D. W.

REF

O.

DN.

UP

DN.

PAN

MEDIA CENTER

2 STORY
GREAT RM.
15/6 X 16/0

DEN
12/2 X 12/0
(9' CLG.)

BUILT-IN

DECK

PLANTER

◄ **40'** ►

©Alan Mascord Design Associates, Inc.

SHOP
8/10 X 8/4

GARAGE
29/8 X 31/10

UP

STORAGE

Plan L02-22109
The Anson

Upper Floor	960 Sq. Ft.
Main Floor	1,302 Sq. Ft.
Total Area	2,262 Sq. Ft.
Incl. Foundation	*Daylight Basement*

Design includes cedar shingle siding, stone foundation accents and a planter box at the offset entry. A sidelight and a transom on the entry door help to brighten the main foyer. Two steps up lead to a two-story great room that is embellished with a built-in media center, an atrium door to a front deck and a two-sided fireplace.

Featuring
iLevel
Trus Joist · Structurwood · Weyerhaeuser

Plan L02-2375
The Tyndall

Upper Floor	925 Sq. Ft.
Main Floor	2,292 Sq. Ft.
Total Area	3,217 Sq. Ft.
Included Foundation	*Crawlspace*

Influenced by the Modernist movement, this California contemporary design is grand in façade and comfortable to live in. Stone, siding, and shingles dress the exterior in tandem with huge window areas and a clever walled patio just at the entry. A two-story foyer opens to the formal dining room (also two-story) and the great room.

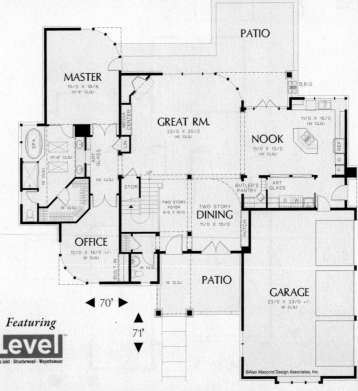

Featuring
iLevel
Trus Joist · Structurwood · Weyerhaeuser

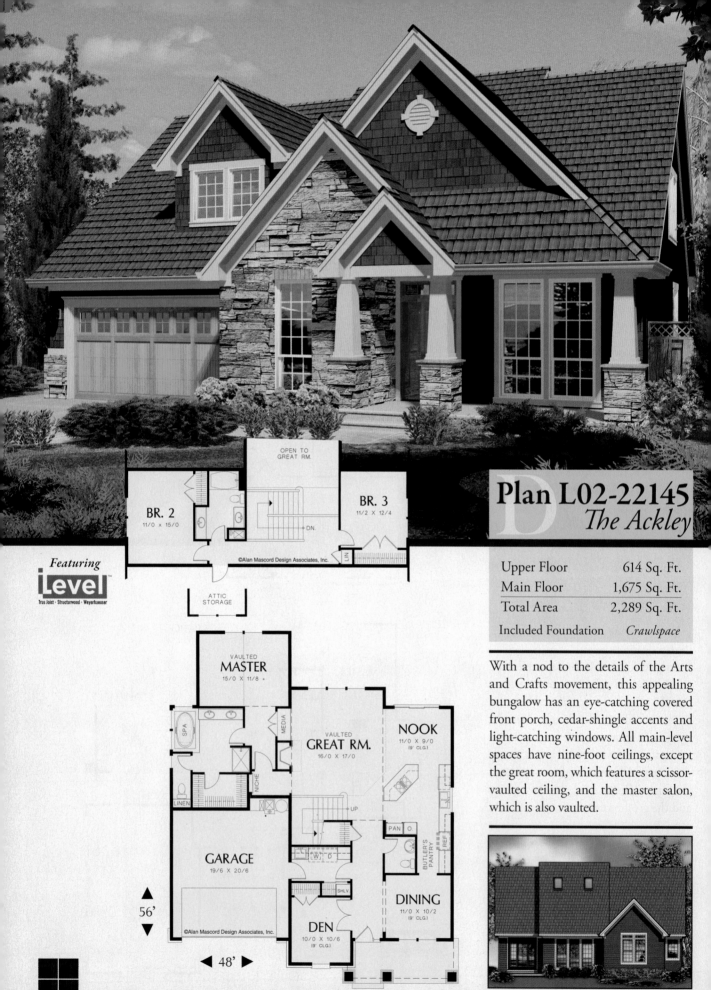

OPEN TO
GREAT RM.

BR. 2
11/0 x 15/0

BR. 3
11/2 X 12/4

DN.

©Alan Mascord Design Associates, Inc.

LIN

ATTIC
STORAGE

VAULTED
MASTER
15/0 X 11/8 +

SPA

MEDIA

NICHE

LINEN

GARAGE
19/6 X 20/6

VAULTED
GREAT RM.
16/0 X 17/0

NOOK
11/0 X 9/0
(9' CLG.)

PAN.

O.

REF

BUTLER'S
PANTRY

UP

SHLV.

DEN
10/0 X 10/6
(9' CLG.)

DINING
11/0 X 10/2
(9' CLG.)

©Alan Mascord Design Associates, Inc.

56'

48'

Plan L02-22145
The Ackley

Upper Floor	614 Sq. Ft.
Main Floor	1,675 Sq. Ft.
Total Area	2,289 Sq. Ft.
Included Foundation	*Crawlspace*

With a nod to the details of the Arts and Crafts movement, this appealing bungalow has an eye-catching covered front porch, cedar-shingle accents and light-catching windows. All main-level spaces have nine-foot ceilings, except the great room, which features a scissor-vaulted ceiling, and the master salon, which is also vaulted.

Featuring
iLevel
Trus Joist · Structurwood · Weyerhaeuser

Plan L02-1201J
The Dawson

Main Floor	1,807 Sq. Ft.
Lower Floor	1,157 Sq. Ft.
Sub-Total	2,964 Sq. Ft.
Bonus Room	+150 Sq. Ft.
Incl. Foundation	*Daylight Basement*

Looking for a character-infused home you can build on a budget? Take a look at this charming bungalow. Just 2,964 square feet, the home's efficiency allows you to control building costs so you can afford to keep its eye-catching details, including carriage-style garage doors, stone-accented foundation.

DECK

VAULTED MASTER
15/0 X 14/0+/-

NOOK
9/8 X 16/8+/-
12/6 X 13/8 +/-

VAULTED GREAT RM.
17/2 X 18/0 +/-

CLAW-FOOT TUB

GARAGE
25/0 X 22/6

DINING
10/6 X 15/0

DEN/BR. 2
VAULTED
15/0 X 10/0+/-

PORCH

©Alan Mascord Design Associates, Inc.

55'-6"

59'-6"

Featuring
iLevel™
Trus Joist · Structurwood · Weyerhaeuser

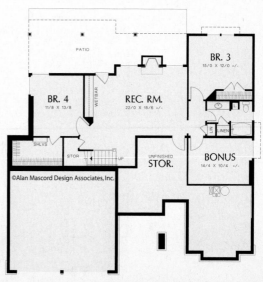

PATIO

BR. 3
15/0 X 12/0 +/-

BR. 4
11/8 X 13/8

REC. RM.
22/0 X 15/6 +/-

WETBAR

SHLVS

STOR

UP

UNFINISHED STOR.

BONUS
14/4 X 10/4 +/-

LIN **LINEN**

©Alan Mascord Design Associates, Inc.

Plan L02-22140
The Landon

Featuring
iLevel™
Trus Joist · Structurwood · Weyerhaeuser

Upper Floor	993 Sq. Ft.
Main Floor	1,171 Sq. Ft.
Total Area	2,164 Sq. Ft.
Included Foundation	*Crawlspace*

The interior revolves around a central hall. The laundry to the right of the entry opens to a three-car garage (or make one bay a shop), with a half-bath and two closets nearby. A home office is on the left — build it with built-in cabinetry or a closet — the choice is yours. The open great room (with fireplace and optional built-ins) and dining area are to the back of the plan.

VAULTED
MASTER
14/0 X 16/0
SPA

OPEN TO BELOW

BR. 3
11/2 X 10/4

LINEN

DN.
OPT BUILT-INS

ATTIC
STORAGE

BR. 2
11/10 X 11/6

©Alan Mascord Design Associates, Inc.

OPTIONAL BUILT-INS

DINING
14/0 X 12/6
(9' CLG.)

VAULTED
GREAT RM.
18/0 X 17/0

14/0 X 12/0
(9' CLG.)

PAN

UP

GARAGE
/SHOP
11/0 X 16/0

DESK
REF

(9' CLG.)

OPT BUILT-INS
OR CLOSET

(10' CLG.)

GARAGE
20/0 X 21/0

D W

OFFICE
11/0 X 14/6 +/-
(9' CLG.)

49'

45'

©Alan Mascord Design Associates, Inc.

Plan L02-2135
The Seville

Upper Floor	477 Sq. Ft.
Main Floor	1,230 Sq. Ft.
Total Area	1,707 Sq. Ft.
Bonus	+195 Sq. Ft.
Included Foundation	*Crawlspace*

A covered front entry, a facade that's trimmed in brick, and tall mullioned windows give this home timeless appeal. Daily life revolves around the large, great room with fireplace. The efficient kitchen is enhanced by an island that adds work surface and storage. The master suite provides a private get-away on the first floor.

Featuring
iLevel
Trus Joist · Structurwood · Weyerhaeuser

BR. 3
12/6 X 12/2 +/-

BR. 2
10/9 X 12/2 +/-

LIN

OPEN TO
GREAT RM.
BELOW

DN.

BONUS RM.
13/6 X 12/6

ATTIC
STORAGE

NOOK
8/8 X 8/10

DINING
9/10 X 10/4

REF

VAULTED
MASTER
16/0 X 11/10

P.

LINEN

SPA

TWO STORY
GREAT RM.
15/10 X 19/8

W D

UP

GARAGE
19/4 X 21/8

◄ 40' ►

▲
53'
▼

©Alan Mascord Design Associates, Inc.

Plan L02-21111A
The Brentwood

Upper Floor	885 Sq. Ft.
Main Floor	1,117 Sq. Ft.
Total Area	2,002 Sq. Ft.
Included Foundation	*Crawlspace*

Like many of the early Craftsman homes, the design is efficient and the footprint is square, which helps control building costs. Living spaces flow together at the rear, and are replete with amenities. The kitchen includes an island counter, the dining room offers a built-in hutch and French doors, and the great room provides a fireplace.

Featuring
iLevel
Trus Joist · Structurwood · Weyerhaeuser

VAULTED
MASTER
14/0 X 12/0+/-

LINEN

DN.

OPEN TO BELOW

BR. 3
10/2 X 11/2

BR. 2
12/6 X 12/2+/-

BUILT-IN

©Alan Mascord Design Associates, Inc.

45'

MEDIA

DINING
11/0 X 13/0
(9' CLG.)

BUILT-INS OR FURNITURE

REF PAN

GREAT RM
16/0 X 16/0
VAULTED

BUILT-INS

STOR

W D

BUILT-IN DESK

GARAGE
19/0 X 22/0

UP
(10' CLG.)

OFFICE
11/0 X 10/8
(9' CLG.)

(10' CLG.)   SEAT

©Alan Mascord Design Associates, Inc.

40'

Plan L02-22122Q
The Northbrook

Upper Floor	675 Sq. Ft.
Main Floor	1,838 Sq. Ft.
Total Area	2,513 Sq. Ft.
Included Foundation	*Crawlspace*

You'll like this home for its easy layout, sun-filled interior, and contemporary appointments. You'll love this home, though, for its facade. Emanating the same classic appeal as the American Farmhouse, the exterior displays charming dormers, simple under-eave brackets, and an engaging wraparound front porch.

Featuring
iLevel™
Trus Joist · Structurwood · Weyerhaeuser

©Alan Mascord Design Associates, Inc.

Upper Floor:
GREAT RM. BELOW
BR. 2 — 10/0 X 12/8 +/-
ATTIC STORAGE
LINEN
UNFINISHED BONUS — 20/2 X 18/2 +/-
LIBRARY — 11/0 X 8/8 +/-
BOOKSHLVS
DN.
OPEN TO BELOW
BR. 3 — 10/6 X 12/0 +/-
SHELF

Main Floor:
MASTER — 13/0 X 16/6, VAULTED (9' CLG.)
SPA
LIN
NOOK — 10/0 X 12/6 (9' CLG.)
PAN
REF
GREAT RM. — 17/6 X 17/4, VAULTED
©Alan Mascord Design Associates, Inc.
SHOP — 16/6 X 8/6
W D
UP
STORAGE
BUILT-INS
GARAGE — 20/0 X 19/6
SHLVS
DEN/BR. 4 — 11/0 X 10/6 (9' CLG.)
VAULTED FOYER
DINING — 10/6 X 12/0 (9' CLG.)

62'

56'

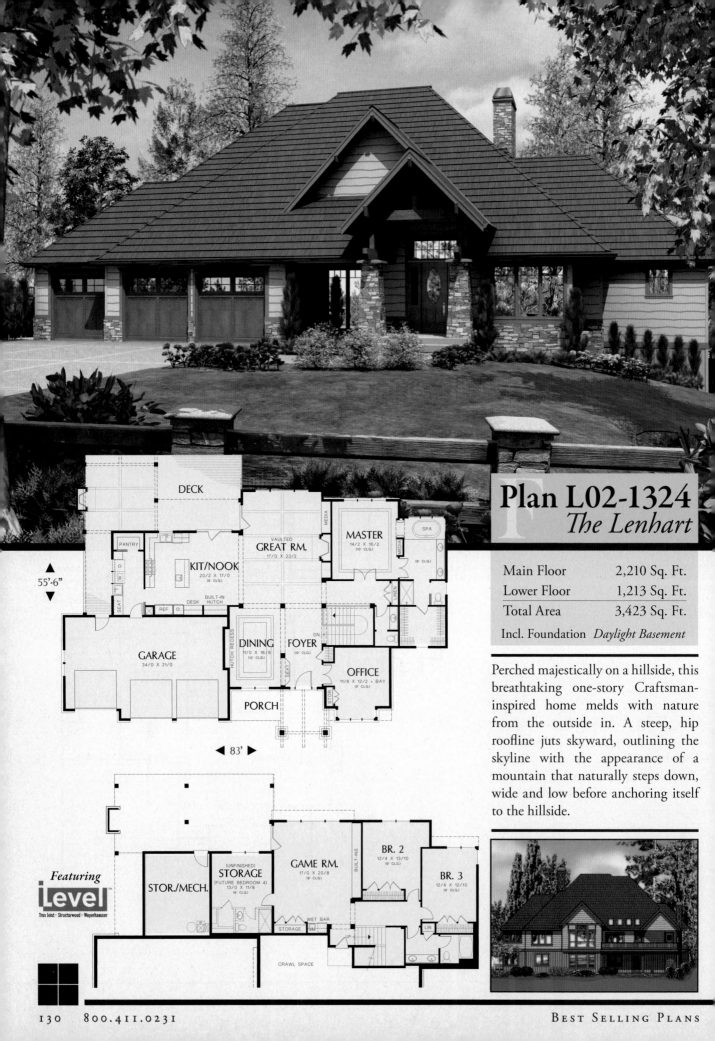

Plan L02-1324
The Lenhart

Main Floor	2,210 Sq. Ft.
Lower Floor	1,213 Sq. Ft.
Total Area	3,423 Sq. Ft.
Incl. Foundation	*Daylight Basement*

Perched majestically on a hillside, this breathtaking one-story Craftsman-inspired home melds with nature from the outside in. A steep, hip roofline juts skyward, outlining the skyline with the appearance of a mountain that naturally steps down, wide and low before anchoring itself to the hillside.

Main Floor Plan Labels:
- DECK
- PANTRY
- KIT/NOOK 20/2 X 17/0 (9' CLG.)
- VAULTED GREAT RM. 17/0 X 23/2
- MEDIA
- MASTER 14/2 X 16/2 (10' CLG.)
- SPA
- SEAT / W / D
- DESK
- REF / O.
- BUILT-IN HUTCH
- HUTCH RECESS
- DINING 11/0 X 16/8 (12' CLG.)
- FOYER (12' CLG.)
- DN.
- LINEN
- (9' CLG.)
- GARAGE 34/0 X 21/0
- OFFICE 11/8 X 12/2 + BAY (9' CLG.)
- PORCH
- SEAT
- STOR.
- 55'-6"
- 83'

Lower Floor Plan Labels:
- STOR./MECH.
- STORAGE (UNFINISHED) (FUTURE BEDROOM 4) 13/0 X 11/8 (9' CLG.)
- GAME RM. 17/0 X 20/8 (9' CLG.)
- BUILT-INS
- BR. 2 12/4 X 13/10 (9' CLG.)
- BR. 3 12/4 X 12/10 (9' CLG.)
- WET BAR
- STORAGE
- UP
- LIN
- CRAWL SPACE

Featuring
iLevel™
Trus Joist · Structurwood · Weyerhaeuser

Plan L02-2377
The Pineville F

Upper Floor	363 Sq. Ft.
Main Floor	2,983 Sq. Ft.
Total Area	3,346 Sq. Ft.
Bonus Room	+652 Sq. Ft.

Included Foundation	*Crawlspace*

A brawny, lodge-style retreat, this home will enhance even the most picturesque setting. Starting with its rugged exterior, the home's shake shingles, wood garage doors, and gable-end brackets join with a stone-accented foundation and a sturdy entrance with flared columns to set a casual tone.

Featuring
iLevel™
Trus Joist · Structurwood · Weyerhaeuser

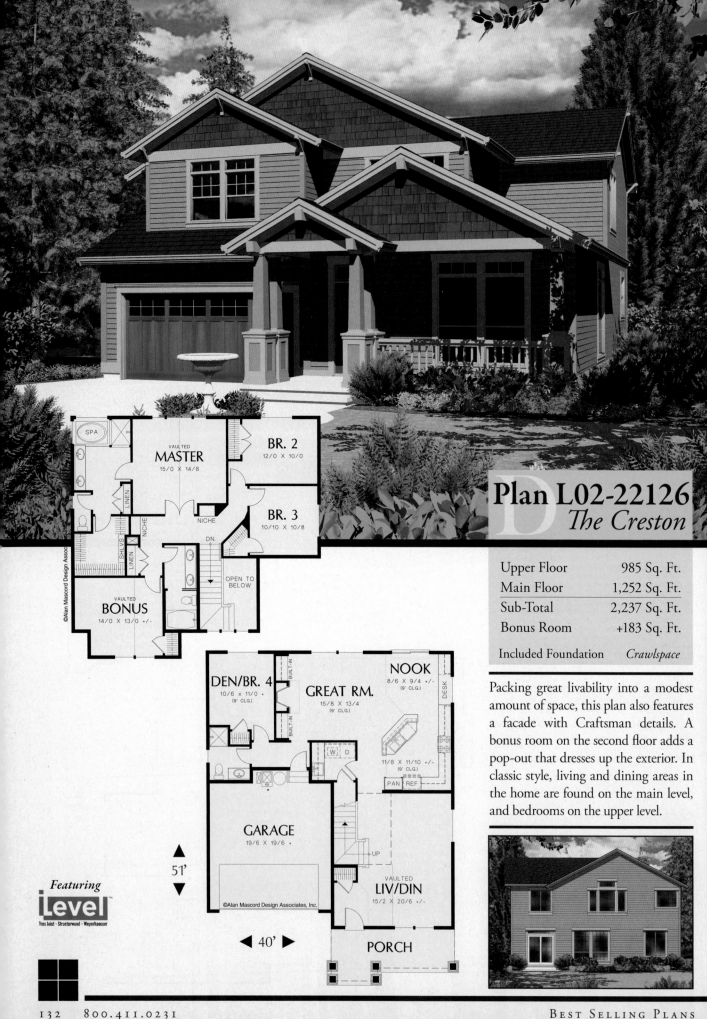

Plan L02-22126
The Creston

Upper Floor	985 Sq. Ft.
Main Floor	1,252 Sq. Ft.
Sub-Total	2,237 Sq. Ft.
Bonus Room	+183 Sq. Ft.

Included Foundation	*Crawlspace*

Packing great livability into a modest amount of space, this plan also features a facade with Craftsman details. A bonus room on the second floor adds a pop-out that dresses up the exterior. In classic style, living and dining areas in the home are found on the main level, and bedrooms on the upper level.

Floor plan labels (upper floor):
- SPA
- VAULTED MASTER 15/0 X 14/8
- BR. 2 12/0 X 10/0
- LINEN
- NICHE
- SHLVS
- LINEN
- NICHE
- BR. 3 10/10 X 10/8
- DN.
- OPEN TO BELOW
- VAULTED BONUS 14/0 X 13/0 +/-
- ©Alan Mascord Design Assoc.

Floor plan labels (main floor):
- DEN/BR. 4 10/6 X 11/0 + (9' CLG.)
- BUILT-IN
- GREAT RM. 15/8 X 13/4 (9' CLG.)
- NOOK 8/6 X 9/4 +/- (9' CLG.)
- DESK
- W D
- 11/8 X 11/10 +/- (9' CLG.)
- PAN REF
- GARAGE 19/6 X 19/6 +
- UP
- VAULTED LIV/DIN 15/2 X 20/6 +/-
- ©Alan Mascord Design Associates, Inc.
- 51'
- 40'
- PORCH

Featuring
iLevel™
Trus Joist · Structurwood · Weyerhaeuser

Plan L02-2346
The Kaiser

Upper Floor	1,110 Sq. Ft.
Main Floor	2,284 Sq. Ft.
Sub-Total	3,394 Sq. Ft.
Bonus Room	+613 Sq. Ft.
Included Foundation	*Crawlspace*

A touch of the rustic trims this sprawling design, with stone foundation accents, white columns, and dormer windows on its facade. A covered porch opens to a two-story foyer with a den on one side and formal dining room on the other. The den contains built-in bookshelves and can double as a bedroom.

Featuring

iLevel™
True Joist · Structurwood · Weyerhaeuser

Plan L02-1220
The Parkview

Main Floor	2,412 Sq. Ft.
Lower Floor	130 Sq. Ft.
Total Area	2,542 Sq. Ft.

Incl. Foundation *Daylight Basement*

If your kitchen is the most popular room in your home, you'll appreciate this split-level home plan with its spacious kitchen and dining nook. The angular island even includes a sit-down snack bar, as well as a cooktop workstation. The dining room with its tall tray ceiling provides a cozy setting.

Featuring
iLevel
Truss Joist · Structurwood · Weyerhaeuser

Floor plan labels:
DECK
DEN 10/8 X 11/8
BR. 3 11/0 X 13/8
BR. 2 13/0 X 11/0
LINEN
UP
DINING 12/0 X 11/4 (12' CLG.)
15/8 X 11/4
DN
D. W.
NICHE
NOOK 11/6 X 12/8
GREAT RM. 20/0 X 20/8 +/- (12' CLG.)
DN UP
MASTER 15/0 X 14/8
MEDIA CENTER
DECK
59'
60'

CRAWLSPACE
15/4 X 7/8
UP
11/4 X 20/10
GARAGE 19/10 X 23/10
©Alan Mascord Design Associates, Inc.

Plan L02-1233
The Cainsville

Main Floor	2,973 Sq. Ft.
Bonus Room	+417 Sq. Ft.

Featuring

iLevel™
Trus Joist · Structurwood · Weyerhaeuser

Included Foundation	*Crawlspace*

Bordering on estate-sized, this plan borrows elements from Norman, Mediterranean and English architecture. The entrance is recessed and framed by a stone chimney stack on one side and a huge arched window on the other. Notable amenities throughout the plan include fireplaces in the great room and master bedroom.

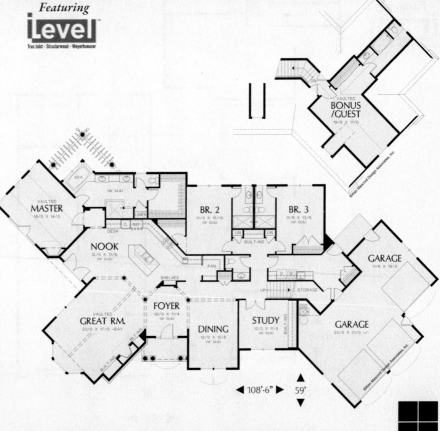

Plan L02-22143A
The Roland

BR. 2
14/4 X 10/0

BR. 3
12/0 X 10/0

LINEN

DN.

ATTIC

VAULTED
BONUS
23/0 X 14/4 +/-

©Alan Mascord Design Associates, Inc.

SPA

VAULTED
MASTER
12/4 X 16/0

VAULTED
DINING
12/0 X 12/6

GARAGE
10/2 X 19/0

VAULTED
GREAT RM
17/6 X 19/0

PAN

W/D

REF

UP

STOR

GARAGE
19/0 X 20/0

VAULTED
OFFICE
10/10 X 11/2

VAULTED
FOYER

8/6 X 13/4

19' CLG.

52'-6"

50'

©Alan Mascord Design Associates, Inc.

Featuring
iLevel™
Trus Joist · Structurwood · Weyerhaeuser

Upper Floor	832 Sq. Ft.
Main Floor	1,464 Sq. Ft.
Total Area	2,296 Sq. Ft.
Included Foundation	*Crawlspace*

A covered porch adds a special touch to this Craftsman home. Its columns are wide and adorned at foundation level by stonework. Additional exterior touches only add to the overall theme: shuttered multi-pane windows, board-and-batten detail in the gable ends and a lovely stone chimney. Interior spaces allow exquisite livability.

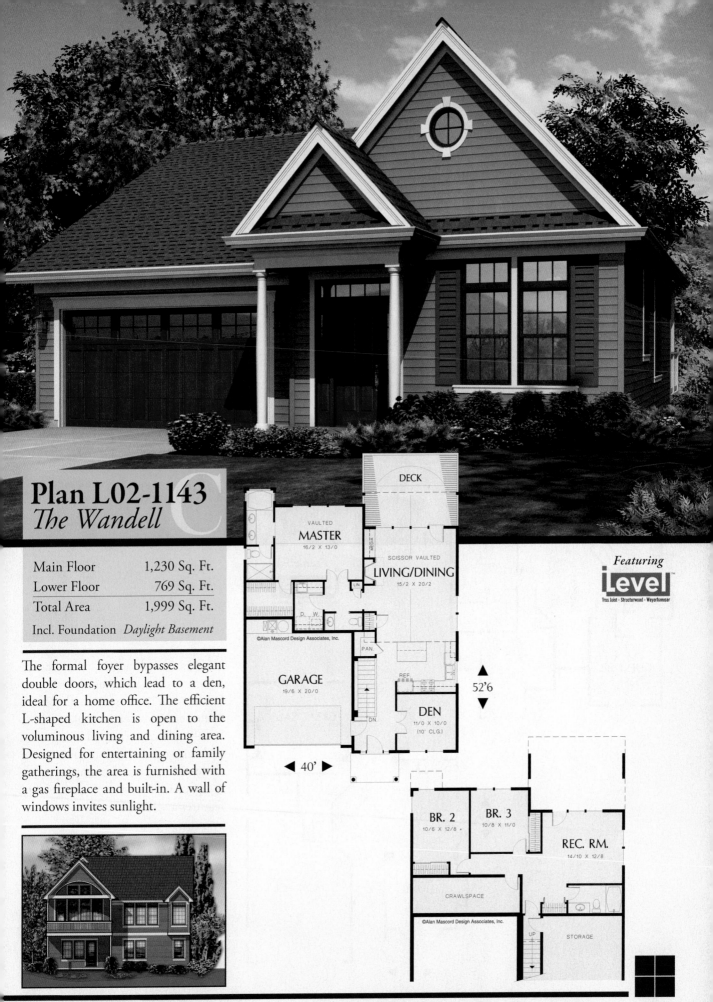

Plan L02-1143
The Wandell C

Main Floor	1,230 Sq. Ft.
Lower Floor	769 Sq. Ft.
Total Area	1,999 Sq. Ft.

Incl. Foundation *Daylight Basement*

The formal foyer bypasses elegant double doors, which lead to a den, ideal for a home office. The efficient L-shaped kitchen is open to the voluminous living and dining area. Designed for entertaining or family gatherings, the area is furnished with a gas fireplace and built-in. A wall of windows invites sunlight.

DECK

VAULTED
MASTER
16/2 X 13/0

SCISSOR VAULTED
LIVING/DINING
15/2 X 20/2

LIN.

D. W.

©Alan Mascord Design Associates, Inc.

PAN.

REF.

GARAGE
19/6 X 20/0

DN.

DEN
11/0 X 10/0
(10' CLG.)

52'6

◄ 40' ►

BR. 2
10/6 X 12/8

BR. 3
10/8 X 11/0

REC. RM.
14/10 X 12/8

CRAWLSPACE

UP

STORAGE

©Alan Mascord Design Associates, Inc.

Featuring
iLevel
Trus Joist · Structurwood · Weyerhaeuser

Plan L02-2223AD
The Sabine

MASTER
VAULTED
15/0 X 15/0 +/-

FAMILY RM.
BELOW

© Alan Mascord Design Associates, Inc.

BR. 2
12/0 X 11/0
(8'-0" CLG)

DN.

FOYER
BELOW

GUEST BR.
VAULTED
13/0 X 12/0 •
(9'-6" CLG)

BR. 3
VAULTED
13/6 X 17/0 +/-
(9'-6" CLG.)

LIN.

Featuring
iLevel™
Trus Joist • Structurwood • Weyerhaeuser

NOOK
10/0 X 15/8
(9' CLG.)

REF.

DESK

BUTLER'S
PANTRY

GREAT RM.
TWO STORY
17/8 X 16/0

MEDIA
CENTER

DINING
12/0 X 11/0
(9' CLG.)

53'

**DEN /
LIVING**
13/0 X 13/8
(9' CLG.)

D. W.

9/0 X 12/0

UP

GARAGE
3 CAR
19/4 X 21/8

42'

© Alan Mascord Design Associates, Inc.

Upper Floor	1,437 Sq. Ft.
Main Floor	1,383 Sq. Ft.
Total Area	2,820 Sq. Ft.
Included Foundation	*Crawlspace*

The main floor is flexible to accommodate the needs of any family. The area next to the entry could serve as a den, complete with a cozy fireplace, or a formal living room with close proximity to the dining room—it's perfect for entertaining. A spacious two-story great room features a second fireplace.

Plan L02-2363B
The Randolf

Upper Floor	1,788 Sq. Ft.
Main Floor	1,835 Sq. Ft.
Total Area	3,623 Sq. Ft.
Included Foundation	*Crawlspace*

Crazy about Craftsman styling? This exquisite plan has it in abundance and doesn't skimp on the floor plan either. Massive stone bases support the Arts-and-Crafts columns at the entry porch. Additional stone detailing adorns the chimneystack and along the foundation line of the main level. A touch of cedar shingle siding and board-and-batten at the gable ends finish the effect.

Featuring
iLevel
Trus Joist · Structurwood · Weyerhaeuser

©Alan Mascord Design Associates, Inc.

MASTER
20/0 X 15/0+

BONUS
15/8 X 12/10

BR. 4
11/0 X 13/10 +/-

SPA

BOOK-CASES

DN.

LINEN

SHLVS

FOYER BELOW

BR. 2
13/0 X 14/0 +/-
(10'-6" CLG)

(8' CLG)

BR. 3
11/8 X 12/10 +/-

FAMILY
15/0 X 17/0 +/-
(9' CLG)

NOOK
10/0 X 14/6
(9' CLG)

(9' CLG)

MEDIA CENTER

BOOKCASES

NICHE

DESK

REF

PAN.

11/6 X 11/6

DEN
12/8 X 12/8 +/-
(9' CLG)

BUTLER'S PANTRY

BENCH

3 CAR
GARAGE
20/6 X 27/6 +/-

LIVING
14/0 X 14/0
(9' CLG)

FOYER

UP

DINING
13/0 X 15/0 +/-
(9' CLG)

©Alan Mascord Design Associates, Inc.

PORCH

52'

◄ 60' ►

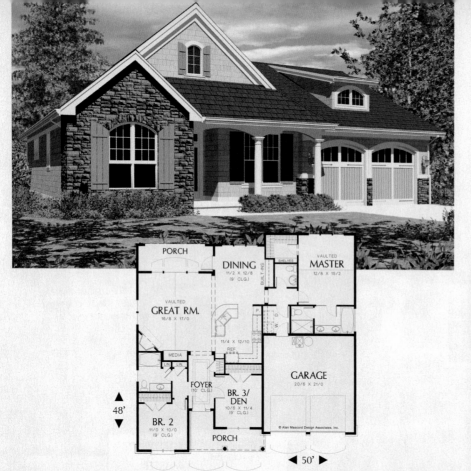

Plan L02-1146
The Godfrey

Total Area   1,580 Sq. Ft.

Included Foundation   *Crawlspace*

Floor plan labels:

PORCH

DINING
11/2 x 12/8
(9' CLG.)

VAULTED
MASTER
12/8 x 15/2

SHELVES

VAULTED
GREAT RM.
16/8 x 17/0

11/4 x 12/10

W D

REF

MEDIA

FOYER
(10' CLG.)

BR. 3/
DEN
10/8 x 11/4
(9' CLG.)

GARAGE
20/6 x 21/0

BR. 2
11/0 x 10/0
(9' CLG.)

PORCH

48'

50'

© Alan Mascord Design Associates, Inc.

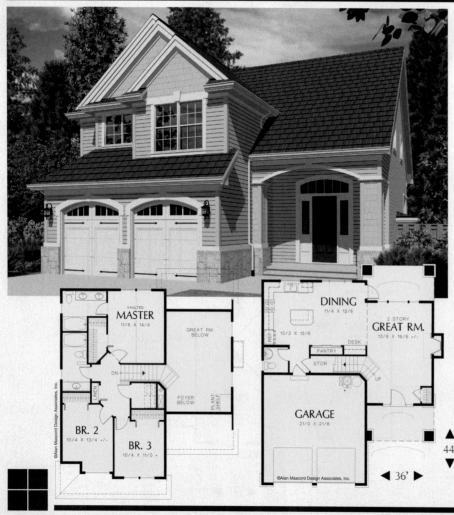

Plan L02-2154F
The Corbett

Upper Floor	784 Sq. Ft.
Main Floor	716 Sq. Ft.
Total Area	1,500 Sq. Ft.

Included Foundation   *Crawlspace*

Floor plan labels:

VAULTED
MASTER
11/8 x 14/4

GREAT RM.
BELOW

DN

LINEN

FOYER
BELOW

PLANT
SHELF

BR. 2
10/4 x 13/4 +/-

BR. 3
10/4 x 11/0

DINING
11/4 x 12/6

2 STORY
GREAT RM.
13/6 x 16/6 +/-

REF

10/2 x 12/6

DESK

PANTRY

STOR

UP

GARAGE
21/0 x 21/6

44'

36'

©Alan Mascord Design Associates, Inc.

Plan L02-1231
The Galen

Total Area   2,001 Sq. Ft.

Included Foundation *Crawlspace*

Plan L02-1149
The Hayword

Total Area   1,728 Sq. Ft.

Included Foundation *Crawlspace*

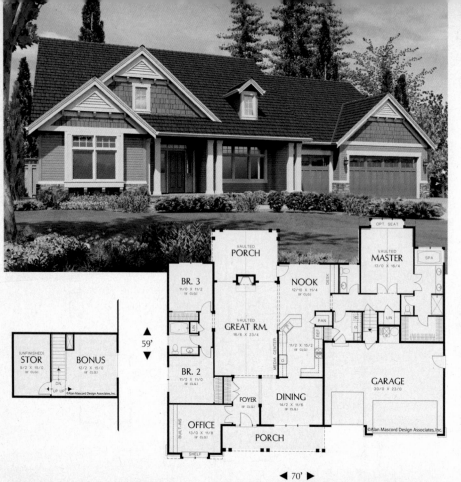

Plan L02-22158
The Willard

Main Floor	2,373 Sq. Ft.
Bonus Room	+226 Sq. Ft.

Included Foundation *Crawlspace*

Plan L02-1144B
The Riverton

Total Area	1,873 Sq. Ft.

Included Foundation *Crawlspace*

BEST SELLING PLANS

Plan L02-21103
The Ellwood

Upper Floor	430 Sq. Ft.
Main Floor	1,514 Sq. Ft.
Total Area	1,944 Sq. Ft.

Included Foundation *Crawlspace*

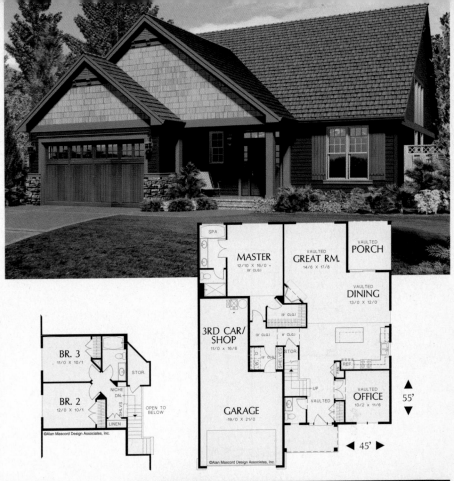

Floor plan labels:
- SPA
- MASTER 12/10 X 16/0 · 19' CLG.)
- VAULTED GREAT RM. 14/6 X 17/8
- VAULTED PORCH
- VAULTED DINING 13/0 X 12/0
- 3RD CAR/SHOP 11/0 x 16/6
- STOR.
- SHELVES
- W/D
- REF
- UP
- VAULTED
- VAULTED OFFICE 10/2 x 11/6
- GARAGE -19/0 X 21/0
- 55'
- 45'
- ©Alan Mascord Design Associates, Inc.

Upper floor labels:
- BR. 3 11/0 X 10/1
- BR. 2 12/0 X 10/1
- STOR.
- NICHE DN.
- PLUS.
- LINEN
- OPEN TO BELOW
- ©Alan Mascord Design Associates, Inc.

Plan L02-2174B
The Monroe

Upper Floor	830 Sq. Ft.
Main Floor	636 Sq. Ft.
Total Area	1,466 Sq. Ft.

Included Foundation *Crawlspace*

Upper floor labels:
- MASTER 14/0 X 11/2
- LIN
- LINEN
- DN.
- BR. 2 9/4 X 11/6
- BR. 3 9/4 X 11/0
- FOYER BELOW
- ©Alan Mascord Design Associates, Inc.

Main floor labels:
- NOOK 9/0 X 10/0
- 7/0 X 11/4
- REF P.
- GREAT RM. 15/0 X 15/0
- GARAGE 19/0 X 21/6 +/-
- UP
- 43'-6"
- 28'
- ©Alan Mascord Design Associates, Inc.

Plan L02-1111AC
The Cypress

Total Area   1,275 Sq. Ft.

Included Foundation   *Crawlspace*

Floor plan labels:

MASTER
VAULTED
13/8 X 11/8

PATIO

BR. 2
10/4 X 10/0
(9' CLG.)

DINING
10/0 X 13/6
(9' CLG.)

BR. 3
10/0 X 10/0
(9' CLG.)

LIVING
VAULTED
14/0 X 14/6

PORCH

GARAGE
19/4 X 21/8

58'

40'

©Alan Mascord Design Associates, Inc.

Plan L02-1152A
The Morton

Total Area   1,800 Sq. Ft.

Included Foundation   *Crawlspace*

Floor plan labels:

PORCH
11/0 X 14/0

DINING
11/6 X 14/8
(9' CLG.)

GREAT RM.
VAULTED
14/6 X 18/6

MASTER
VAULTED
12/2 X 16/2

GARAGE
10/0 X 16/6

SPA

SHLVS

14/0 X 9/4
(9' CLG.)

DESK
REF

GARAGE
19/0 X 19/6

BR. 2
10/8 X 11/6
(9' CLG.)

STORAGE

OFFICE
/BR. 3
12/0 X 12/4
(9' CLG.)

59'

50'

©Alan Mascord Design Associates, Inc.

Plan L02-1154
The Ellington

Total Area   1,891 Sq. Ft.

Included Foundation   *Crawlspace*

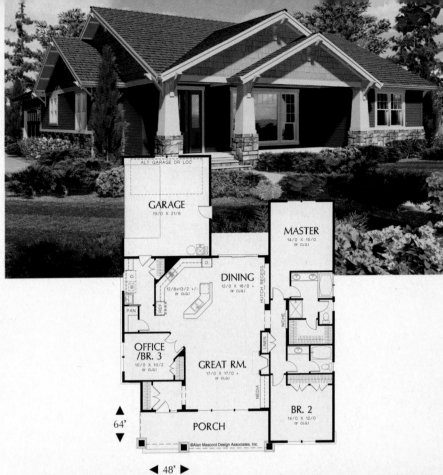

GARAGE
19/0 X 21/6

ALT GARAGE DR LOC

MASTER
14/0 X 15/0
(9' CLG.)

DINING
12/0 X 16/0
(9' CLG.)

HUTCH RECESS

12/8x13/2
(9' CLG.)

PAN

REF

W
D

NICHE

LINEN

OFFICE /BR. 3
10/0 X 10/2
(9' CLG.)

GREAT RM.
17/0 X 17/0 +
(9' CLG.)

MEDIA

BR. 2
14/0 X 12/0
(9' CLG.)

64'

PORCH

©Alan Mascord Design Associates, Inc.

48'

Plan L02-1230
The Renville

Total Area   2,367 Sq. Ft.

Included Foundation   *Crawlspace*

GARAGE
21/0 X 28/6

SPA
(9' CLG.)

DESK

14/2 X 4/0

NOOK
10/6 X 9/0
(11' CLG.)

PORCH

MASTER
14/8 X 17/8

REF

GREAT RM.
19/8 X 16/8
(11' CLG.)

MEDIA CENTER

VAULTED

D W

10/8 X 11/0
(11' CLG.)

LIN

©Alan Mascord Design Associates, Inc.

BR. 3
11/8 X 13/8
(9' CLG.)

BR. 2
11/0 X 12/0
(9' CLG.)

SHLVS

PAN
(9' CLG.)

BUTLER'S PANTRY

DINING
13/0 X 11/0
(11' CLG.)

FOYER
(11' CLG.)

NICHE

BOOKCASE

DEN
15/0 X 12/0
(9' CLG.)

62'

PORCH

DN.

72'

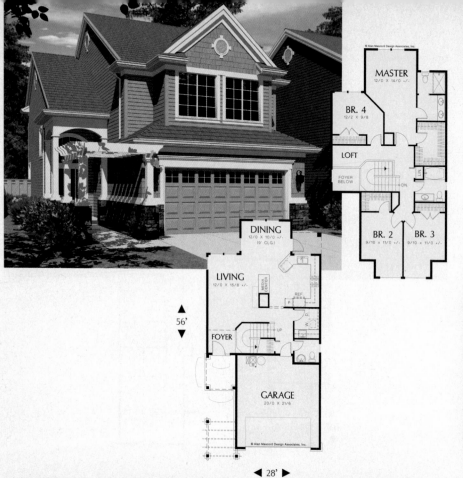

Plan L02-2198
The Moraine

Upper Floor	1,129 Sq. Ft.
Main Floor	790 Sq. Ft.
Total Area	1,919 Sq. Ft.

Included Foundation   *Crawlspace*

Plan L02-22148
The Sentinel

Upper Floor	479 Sq. Ft.
Main Floor	1,601 Sq. Ft.
Total Area	2,080 Sq. Ft.

Included Foundation   *Crawlspace*

Plan L02-22137B
The Webster

Upper Floor	1,264 Sq. Ft.
Main Floor	1,269 Sq. Ft.
Total Area	2,533 Sq. Ft.
Bonus Room	+225 Sq. Ft.

Included Foundation *Crawlspace*

Plan L02-2211C
The Stanwood

Upper Floor	1,155 Sq. Ft.
Main Floor	1,321 Sq. Ft.
Total Area	2,476 Sq. Ft.

Included Foundation *Crawlspace*

Plan L02-2199
The Sylvan

Upper Floor	747 Sq. Ft.
Main Floor	951 Sq. Ft.
Sub-Total	1,698 Sq. Ft.
Bonus Room	+254 Sq. Ft.

Included Foundation *Crawlspace*

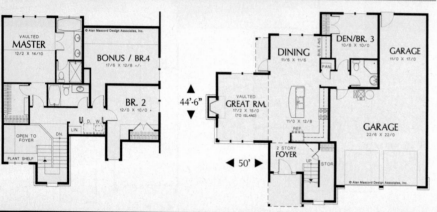

Plan L02-2185A
The Chandler

Upper Floor	668 Sq. Ft.
Main Floor	1,198 Sq. Ft.
Total Area	1,866 Sq. Ft.

Included Foundation *Crawlspace*

Plan L02-22109A
The Jenkins

Upper Floor	960 Sq. Ft.
Main Floor	1,312 Sq. Ft.
Total Area	2,272 Sq. Ft.

Incl. Foundation *Daylight Basement*

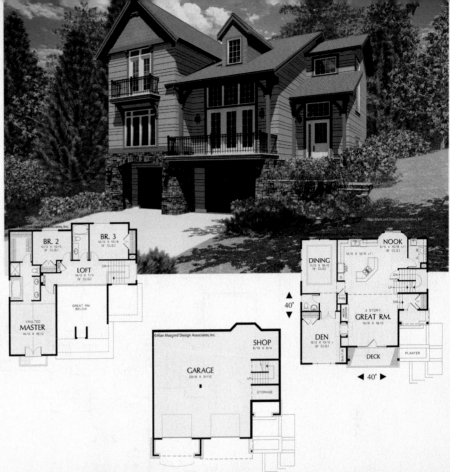

Plan L02-2362
The Leesville

Upper Floor	1,235 Sq. Ft.
Main Floor	2,222 Sq. Ft.
Total Area	3,457 Sq. Ft.

Included Foundation *Crawlspace*

Plan L02-2372
The Bedford

Upper Floor	626 Sq. Ft.
Main Floor	2,440 Sq. Ft.
Sub-Total	3,066 Sq. Ft.
Bonus Room	+302 Sq. Ft.

Included Foundation *Crawlspace*

Plan L02-2218E
The Fulton

Upper Floor	938 Sq. Ft.
Main Floor	1,266 Sq. Ft.
Sub-Total	2,204 Sq. Ft.
Bonus Room	+196 Sq. Ft.

Included Foundation *Crawlspace*

Plan L02-1137
The Summerwood

Sub-Total	1,632 Sq. Ft.
Bonus Room	+1,043

Included Foundation   *Slab*

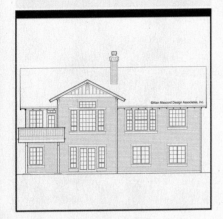

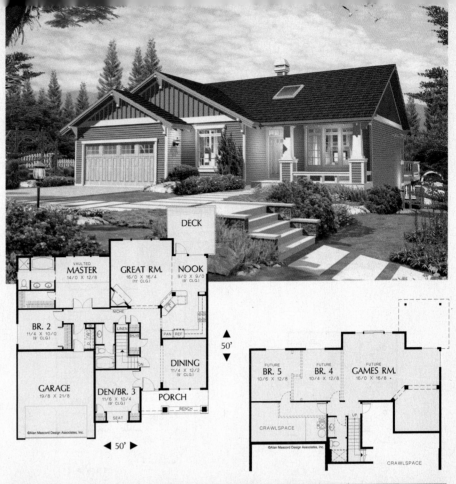

Plan L02-22141A
The Brownsdale

Upper Floor	1,196 Sq. Ft.
Main Floor	1,342 Sq. Ft.
Sub-Total	2,538 Sq. Ft.
Bonus Room	+227 Sq. Ft.

Included Foundation   *Crawlspace*

Plan L02-2229A
The Stratford

Upper Floor	1,025 Sq. Ft.
Main Floor	1,337 Sq. Ft.
Total Area	2,362 Sq. Ft.

Included Foundation   *Crawlspace*

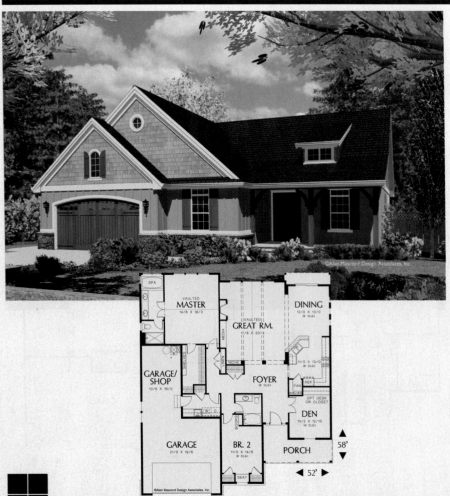

Plan L02-1150
The Lindley

Total Area	1,975 Sq. Ft.

Included Foundation   *Crawlspace*

Plan L02-1326
The Mensing

Main Floor	2,114 Sq. Ft.
Lower Floor	1,345 Sq. Ft.
Total Area	3,459 Sq. Ft.

Incl. Foundation *Daylight Basement*

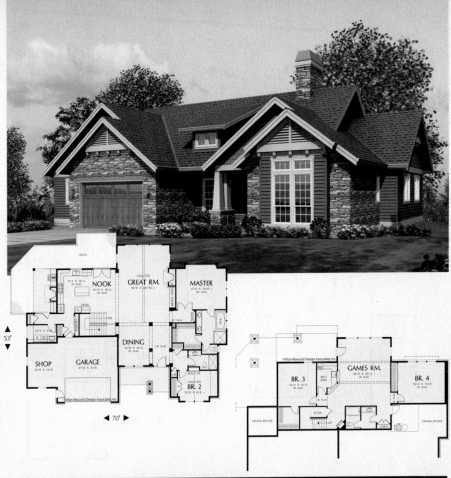

Plan L02-22162
The Crawford

Upper Floor	1,072 Sq. Ft.
Main Floor	1,028 Sq. Ft.
Total Area	2,100 Sq. Ft.

Included Foundation *Crawlspace*

Plan L02-22166
The Tanglewood

Upper Floor	628 Sq. Ft.
Main Floor	1,879 Sq. Ft.
Total Area	2,507 Sq. Ft.

Included Foundation *Crawlspace*

Plan L02-22135
The Greensburg

Upper Floor	1,005 Sq. Ft.
Main Floor	1,950 Sq. Ft.
Total Area	2,955 Sq. Ft.

Included Foundation *Crawlspace*

Plan L02-22146A
The Dellwood

Upper Floor	729 Sq. Ft.
Main Floor	1,574 Sq. Ft.
Total Area	2,303 Sq. Ft.

Included Foundation *Crawlspace*

Upper floor plan:
- GREAT RM. BELLOW
- BR. 3 — 12/0 X 11/0
- BR. 2 — 10/0 X 12/0
- STUDY AREA
- BONUS/ BR. 4 — 12/2 X 12/6
- OPTIONAL CLOSET
- DN.
- ©Alan Mascord Design Associates, Inc.

Main floor plan:
- GREAT RM. — 17/0 X 18/6 (VAULTED)
- DINING — 12/0 X 14/4
- MASTER — 12/0 X 17/4 +/- (VAULTED)
- GARAGE — 10/6 X 15/0
- GARAGE — 23/0 X 22/0 +/-
- STORAGE
- FOYER
- DEN/ BR. 5 — 10/0 X 12/0
- SPA, REF, PAN, SHLVS, UP
- OPTIONAL BUILT-INS
- ©Alan Mascord Design Associates, Inc.

47' × 54'

Plan L02-1232
The Garrett

Total Area	2,650 Sq. Ft.

Included Foundation *Crawlspace*

Floor plan:
- OFFICE — 12/8 X 11/8
- BR. 3 — 12/0 X 11/4
- BR. 2 — 12/0 X 11/4
- 8/0 X 17/6
- GARAGE — 20/6 X 33/0
- LINEN
- NOOK — 11/6 X 12/8
- DINING — 14/0 X 12/0 (VAULTED)
- 15/8 X 11/4
- GREAT RM. — 18/0 X 22/0 (VAULTED)
- MASTER — 16/0 X 13/8 (VAULTED)
- SPA
- ©Alan Mascord Design Associates, Inc.

94' × 53'

Your Plan Set Includes...

· Exterior Elevations

Front, rear, left and right sides of the house. Shows materials, details and measurements at ¼" scale.

· Detailed Floor Plans

Show the layout of the house. Rooms and interior spaces are carefully dimensioned, windows and door sizes are noted. These plans show the location of kitchen appliances and bathroom fixtures.

· Electrical Layout

Usually included on the floor plan, shows suggested locations for electrical fixtures and outlets.

· Interior and Cabinet Elevations

These drawings show specific details and dimensions of cabinets in the kitchen, laundry room, and bathrooms. Also provides views of the fireplaces, bookcases, and built-in units.

· Foundation Plan

This plan gives the foundation layout, including support walls, excavated and unexcavated areas, if any, dimensions, notes and details. Crawlspace is our standard foundation but basement and slabs are available.

· Typical Wall Section

Shows how the walls are constructed from footer to rafter. This section specifies the home's construction, insulation, flooring and roofing details.

· Building Sections

Important changes in floor, ceiling and roof heights or the relationship of one level to another are called out and illustrated.

· General Notes/Details

This page provides, in more detail, how to construct certain components of your home such as the roof system, stairs and deck.

· Roof Plan

Shows the overall layout and necessary details for roof construction with structural sizes. If trusses are used, it is suggested that you work with your local truss manufacturer to design your trusses to comply with local codes.

Optional Add Ons...

· Structural Floor Framing Plan Provided by

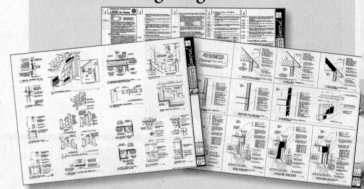

Shows floor framing necessary for construction and suitable for submission to local building departments. Available for every new plan in our collection. Please call to verify availability.

FREE with any plan purchase.

Efficient Living Program

· Notes & Details (Green (G) Sheets)

These pages describe, in detail, how to construct your home to meet green building standards. Choose from two national certification tracks: LEED® or NGBS™ or a generic specification for local or uncertified projects.

· Mascord Efficient Living Information Packet

Information you need to build your home to be sustainable and healthy. This includes details about certification tracks, homeowners information packet, forms to give vendors, calculations, and the required forms necessary to certify your home.

· Consultation

Includes one-hour phone conference or personal meeting with a Mascord Green Team member to get you on track and to answer any questions.

Initial Package Purchase (includes book and CD-ROM) $250

Subsequent Package Purchases $200

Repeat Package Purchase $100

2008 Prices

	A	B	C	D	E	F	G	H	J	K	L
Bid Set *¼"-Stamped "Not for Construction"* *Full credit toward plan purchase*	$250	475	525	575	625	695	750	850	950	1,100	1,325
5 Set Package	$325	550	595	625	675	750	825	925	1,075	1,325	1,675
8 Set Package	$350	595	650	700	775	850	950	1,050	1,150	1,400	1,750
Vellum-Single Use *Need signed license agreement* *and legal description of lot*	$395	800	850	925	1,050	1,200	1,300	1,450	1,750	2,000	2,400
CAD File-Single Use *Need signed license agreement and* *legal description of lot*	$850	1,350	1,450	1,575	1,700	1,850	2,000	2,175	2,400	2,800	3,300
Upgrade to Multiple Use *from Vellum or CAD* *Need signed license agreement*	$250	450	475	500	525	575	625	700	800	950	1,100
Basement Foundation	n/a	$195	225	250	275	295	325	350	375	395	425
Slab Foundation	n/a	$80	95	105	125	140	160	185	215	250	300
Materials List	$55	70	75	80	90	100	115	135	175	225	350

Efficient Living

- 1st Plan Purchase **$250**- *Includes Listing on website, plan specific Green sheets, copy of the Green book, information packet, and 1 hour consultation*
- 2nd Plan Purchase **$200**- *Includes plan specific Green sheets, information packet, and 1/2 hour consultation*
- Repeat of same plan **$100**- *Includes plan specific Green sheets, information packet, and 1/2 hour consultation*

	A	B	C	D	E	F	G	H	J	K	L
Extra Stock Plan Sets *Only with plan purchase*	$20	25	25	30	30	35	35	40	40	50	50

Full Reverse Sets $75 per order
Text Reads Correctly

Shipping & Handling $15—Ground $35—2nd Day Air $65—Overnight ($50 in OR, WA)

Now Available!
MASCORD EFFICIENT LIVING BOOK
Only **$14.95**
Includes over 50 plans, that meet Green Building Standards.
Includes CD-ROM.

The Plans

As a minimum, our homes our designed for 25 psf snow load, 2 x 6 exterior walls with R-21 insulation, and ceiling insulation shown as R-38 at flat areas and R-30 at vaulted areas. Regional construction practices may necessitate alteration of the drawings. Consult a local designer or engineer. A set of reproducibles or CAD files are available to facilitate this process.

The plans in the Mascord Collection are protected under the Federal Copyright Act, Title 17 of the United States Code. The purchaser agrees that the use of the plan is for one time only and that the plan or any part of it will not be repoduced by any means without the written consent of the copyright owner. Multi-use licenses are available.

Although we make every effort to ensure the accuracy of our plan information, we reserve the right to make any necessary changes to correct mistakes or make the plan comply with new building codes. Sometimes these changes will result in minor square footage discrepancies.

All prices and specifications are subject to changes without notice. Not responsible for typographic errors. Check your local building codes for design compliance and suitability on your particular site. All sales are final.

Order Now... 5 Easy Ways!

1. Call Us
800/411-0231
503/225-9161 Portland
8am-5pm, M-F, PST

2. Fax Us
503/225-0933

3. On Line
www.mascordlivingspaces.com
email sales@mascord.com

4. By Mail
1305 NW 18th Ave.
Portland, OR 97209

5. In Person
- 1305 NW 18th Ave.
  Portland, OR

- 1000 Oakesdale Ave.
  Suite 115
  Renton, WA

Pre-order your copy of

mascord **efficient**living

Only $14.95

mascord **efficient**living

Build a more Sustainable Lifestyle

foreword by Sarah Susanka, FAIA

DIGITAL GREEN™ PORTFOLIO   Google

1.800.411.0231

available March 18th

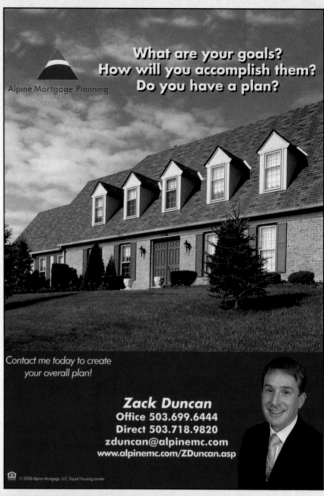

What are your goals?
How will you accomplish them?
Do you have a plan?

Alpine Mortgage Planning

Contact me today to create
your overall plan!

Zack Duncan
Office 503.699.6444
Direct 503.718.9820
zduncan@alpinemc.com
www.alpinemc.com/ZDuncan.asp

© 2008 Alpine Mortgage, LLC. Equal Housing Lender

ROWELL ENGINEERING & DESIGN, INC.

Civil Structural Engineering

Providing wind/seismic engineering in Oregon
& Washington since 1993

New Engineering for 2008!

Less material, less hardware,
less cost, less confusion!

More Value!

Order your lateral engineering by April 1, 2008
and receive a $50 discount.
Mention RED081 when you place your order

Call for more information about our new
engineering program!

(503) 254-6292

10570 SE Washington St., Suite 210
Portland, OR 97216

THE SESSA CORPORATION

www.sessacorp.com

Supporting residential builders since 1984

Structural Engineering & Detailing

A full service engineering, design, & detailing company

Our services include site specific:

Vertical Load Analysis & Framing Plans

Lateral Load Analysis & Shear Wall Plans

Foundation Design and Detailing

Offering Stamps in:

Arizona, California, Colorado, Connecticut, Idaho, Maryland, Massachusetts, Michigan, Montana, New York, Oregon, Pennsylvania, Virginia & Washington

4005 134th Place, SE · Mill Creek, WA 98012 · (425) 379-8951 · Fax (425) 379-8952

**WINSTEAD AND ASSOCIATES, AIA
ARCHITECTURE AND BUILDING
CODE SERVICES, PC**

714 Main Street
Oregon City, OR
97045
T (503) 723-8003
F (503) 723-0578

Stephen M. Winstead, AIA

Architectural Services
Specializing in:

- Plan Review and
  Building Inspection

- General Building Code
  Information

- Building Code Training

- Commercial
  Architecture

- Multi-family residence
  alterations

www.winsteadandassociates.com
info@winsteadandassociates.com

BUILD
REMODEL
HOME REPAIR

Roofing
Siding & Decking
Doors & Windows
Wood & Laminate
Flooring

10% Off
when you mention this ad

YOUR 1ST CHOICE
FOR HOME SERVICES

pro BILT INC.
CONSTRUCTION & REMODELING

CALL **503.758.4816**

Serving Portland, Oregon and surrounding areas
Licenced, Bonded and Insured   CCB#174994

The Beauty of Choice.

Lakeside Lumber offers a wide variety of decking and siding materials to suit your lifestyle and your taste. We're always adding new, innovative products such as Castia Stone and low-maintenance, composite decking. And, of course, we carry a wide selection of beautiful, natural wood. Since 1937, we've supplied siding and decking products for homes across the Northwest. Visit our online gallery at **www.lakesidelumber.com or come see our showroom** to learn more about our superior products and service.

Lakeside Lumber

Siding & Decking Specialists
Toll-free: 1-888-999-8405
www.lakesidelumber.com

PROUD MEMBER

HBA
Home Builders Association
of Metropolitan Portland